INTRODUCTION TO FUNCTION ALGEBRAS

MATHEMATICS LECTURE NOTE SERIES

E. Artin and J. Tate	CLASS FIELD THEORY
Michael Atiyah	K-THEORY
Hyman Bass	ALGEBRAIC K-THEORY
Melvyn S. Berger Marion S. Berger	PERSPECTIVES IN NONLINEARITY
Armand Borel	LINEAR ALGEBRAIC GROUPS
Andrew Browder	INTRODUCTION TO FUNCTION ALGEBRAS
Paul J. Cohen	SET THEORY AND THE CONTINUUM HYPOTHESIS
Eldon Dyer	COHOMOLOGY THEORIES
Walter Feit	CHARACTERS OF FINITE GROUPS
John Fogarty	INVARIANT THEORY
William Fulton	ALGEBRAIC CURVES
Marvin J. Greenberg	LECTURES ON ALGEBRAIC TOPOLOGY
Marvin J. Greenberg	LECTURES ON FORMS IN MANY VARIABLES
Robin Hartshorne	FOUNDATIONS OF PROJECTIVE GEOMETRY
J. F. P. Hudson	PIECEWISE LINEAR TOPOLOGY
Irving Kaplansky	RINGS OF OPERATORS
K. Kapp and H. Schneider	COMPLETELY O-SIMPLE SEMIGROUPS
Joseph B. Keller Stuart Antman	BIFURCATION THEORY AND NONLINEAR EIGENVALUE PROBLEMS
Serge Lang	ALGEBRAIC FUNCTIONS
Serge Lang	RAPPORT SUR LA COHOMOLOGIE DES GROUPES
Ottmar Loos	SYMMETRIC SPACES I: GENERAL THEORY II: COMPACT SPACES AND CLASSIFICATION

I. G. Macdonald	ALGEBRAIC GEOMETRY: INTRODUCTION TO SCHEMES
George W. Mackey	INDUCED REPRESENTATIONS OF GROUPS AND QUANTUM MECHANICS
Andrew Ogg	MODULAR FORMS AND DIRICHLET SERIES
Richard Palais	FOUNDATIONS OF GLOBAL NON-LINEAR ANALYSIS
William Parry	ENTROPY AND GENERATORS IN ERGODIC THEORY
D. S. Passman	PERMUTATION GROUPS
Walter Rudin	FUNCTION THEORY IN POLYDISCS
Jean-Pierre Serre	ABELIAN *l*-ADIC REPRESENTATIONS AND ELLIPTIC CURVES
Jean-Pierre Serre	ALGEBRES DE LIE SEMI-SIMPLE COMPLEXES
Jean-Pierre Serre	LIE ALGEBRAS AND LIE GROUPS
Shlomo Sternberg	CELESTIAL MECHANICS

A Note from the Publisher

This volume was printed directly from a typescript prepared by the author, who takes full responsibility for its content and appearance. The Publisher has not performed his usual functions of reviewing, editing, typesetting, and proofreading the material prior to publication.

The Publisher fully endorses this informal and quick method of publishing lecture notes at a moderate price, and he wishes to thank the author for preparing the material for publication.

INTRODUCTION TO FUNCTION ALGEBRAS

ANDREW BROWDER

Brown University

W. A. BENJAMIN, INC.

New York 1969 Amsterdam

INTRODUCTION TO FUNCTION ALGEBRAS

Library of Congress Catalog Card number 68-59248
Manufactured in the United States of America
12345MR32109

*The manuscript was put into production on February 13, 1969,
this volume was published on March 15, 1969*

W. A. BENJAMIN, INC.
New York, New York 10016

INTRODUCTION

The subject of function algebras has been receiving an increasing amount of attention in recent years. Several excellent survey articles have appeared, by Wermer, Hoffman, Royden, and perhaps others, but there seems to be a place for a volume which gives a detailed account of some of the more important results and methods, without attempting the depth of coverage of a treatise such as Gamelin's book [2], soon to appear.

The theory of function algebras draws from two sources: functional analysis, and the theory of analytic functions of several complex variables. The reader may turn to the first chapter of the book of Gunning and Rossi [1], or to Hörmander [1], for an introduction to function algebras from the point of view of several complex variables. This volume is meant to expound on some of the applications of functional analysis, with only a few indications given as to the relevance of several complex variables. We envision the reader as a graduate student, or mathematician with another specialty, who knows a reasonable amount of integration theory and functional analysis in the abstract, without necessarily having seen many applications. Among our purposes is to show him the theorems of Riesz, Banach and their successors being applied, and to show him some of the Banach space framework in which classical function theory rests. The beautiful idea of Frigyes Riesz, to study approximation problems by passing to the dual space, still has a large amount of energy left, and the pages that follow will show some of the ways in which this idea has flourished a half century after its inception. The Poisson formula, the Schwarz-Pick lemma, Jensen's inequality, Hadamard's three circles theorem, these and other classical results have abstract formulations, an acquaintance with which can only enrich one's mathematical culture.

This book is based largely on lectures given at Brown University in the spring of 1966, to a class consisting mainly of second-year graduate students. The background necessary for reading the book is then the background of these students, who had taken the usual year courses in real and complex analysis, plus a semester course in functional analysis. The usual introductory courses in analysis are by now sufficiently standardized so that little need be said about them. Today, every second year graduate student can be expected to know the basic results of Banach space theory: the Hahn-Banach theorem, open mapping and closed graph theorems, uniform boundedness principle. We shall expect, in addition, a familiarity with the separation theorem (the best form of the Hahn-Banach theorem), the weak-* topology in the dual space of a Banach space, the Banach-Alaoglu theorem (if B is a Banach space, the closed unit ball in B* is weak-* compact) and its converse, the Banach-Krein-Smulian theorem (a subspace of B* is weak-* closed if its intersection with the closed unit ball is weak-* compact). At one or two places, we use the theorem that an operator between Banach spaces has closed range if and only if its adjoint does; the range of the adjoint is closed if and only if it is weak-* closed. We will also need the Krein-Milman theorem. A convenient source for all this is the book of Dunford and Schwartz [1].

Because of the limited size of this book, and my desire to give arguments in full detail whenever possible, many important topics are only mentioned in passing, with a reference, and many interesting results, and their authors, do not get mentioned at all. The choice of what to include or leave out has been highly subjective. In addition, the history of the subject that the reader may glean from this book is distorted. While I have made an effort to attribute theorems correctly, I am aware that important contributions have been slighted. Many results appear without attribution. In some cases, these are results which were found independently by a large enough number of people, or received enough oral circulation prior to publication to merit being placed in the category of mathematical folklore. In other cases, I have simply not been able to determine who exactly proved what, and when.

I wish to thank Alfred Hallstrom, Eva Kallin, Kenneth Preskenis, and John Wermer for reading the manuscript and making valuable comments. My thanks go also to Mrs Roberta Weller and Mrs. Evelyn Kapuscinski, who carried out the arduous job of preparing the camera copy.

TABLE OF CONTENTS

Chapter One: Banach Algebras

1-1	Function algebras	1
1-2	Banach algebras	8
1-3	The maximal ideal spaces of some examples	29
1-4	The functional calculus	46
1-5	Analytic structure	56
1-6	Point derivations	63

Chapter Two: Measures

2-1	Representing and annihilating measures	79
2-2	The Choquet boundary	87
2-3	Peak points	96
2-4	Peak sets and interpolation	102
2-5	Representing measures and the Jensen inequality	114

2-6 Representing measures and Schwarz's lemma 127
2-7 Antisymmetric algebras 136
2-8 The essential set 144

Chapter Three: Rational Approximation

3-1 Preliminaries 149
3-2 Annihilating measures for R(X) 158
3-3 Representing measures for R(X) 170
3-4 Harmonic functions 179
3-5 The algebras A(X) and A_X 195

Chapter Four: Dirichlet Algebras

4-1 Dirichlet algebras 207
4-2 Annihilating measures 215
4-3 Applications 228
4-4 Analytic structure in the maximal ideal space 243

Appendix: Cole's Counterexample to the Peak Point Conjecture 255

Bibliography 263

CHAPTER ONE

BANACH ALGEBRAS

1-1 FUNCTION ALGEBRAS

Let X be a compact topological space. We denote by C(X) the set of all continuous functions from X to the complex field $\mathbb{C}$. For $s \in \mathbb{C}$, we shall denote by the same letter s the constant function which takes only the value s on X. If we define addition and multiplication to be the pointwise operations, C(X) is a commutative associative algebra over $\mathbb{C}$. For $f \in C(X)$, we define $\|f\| = \sup\{|f(x)| : x \in X\}$; if $K \subset X$, we put $\|f\|_K$ to be $\sup\{|f(x)| : x \in K\}$ (thus $\|f\| = \|f\|_X$). It is an elementary theorem of analysis that if $\{f_n\}$ is a Cauchy sequence with respect to this norm, i.e., if $\|f_n - f_m\| \to 0$ as $n, m \to \infty$, then $\{f_n\}$ converges, i.e., then there exists $f \in C(X)$ such that $\|f_n - f\| \to 0$. Thus $C(X)$ is a Banach space with this sup norm. We note that $\|fg\| \leq \|f\| \cdot \|g\|$ for all $f, g \in C(X)$, and that $\|1\| = 1$.

If $\mathcal{F}$ is a set of functions on a space X, we say that $\mathcal{F}$ *separates the points of* X if for every $x, y \in X$, $x \neq y$, there exists $f \in \mathcal{F}$ such that $f(x) \neq f(y)$.

DEFINITION: We say that A is a function algebra on X if:

i) X is a compact topological space;

ii) $A \subset C(X)$, and A separates the points of X;

iii) $1 \in A$;

iv) A is a closed subalgebra of $C(X)$.

We observe that ii) implies that X is Hausdorff, and that i) and ii) together imply that the given topology of X is equal to the weak A topology (the weakest topology on X for which every function in A is continuous). For if $\mathcal{G}$ and $\mathcal{W}$ denote the topologies, the identity map of $(X, \mathcal{G}) \to (X, \mathcal{W})$ is continuous, and $(X, \mathcal{W})$ is Hausdorff by ii); since $(X,\mathcal{G})$ is compact, the map is a homeomorphism.

If X is a compact Hausdorff space, $C(X)$ is a function algebra on X. Here are some other examples:

Let X be a compact subset of $\mathbb{C}$. We denote by $P(X)$ the set of all continuous functions on X which can be uniformly approximated on X by polynomials in z. Here, and throughout this book, z denotes the identity function of $\mathbb{C} \to \mathbb{C}$, or its restrictions.

More generally, if X is a compact subset of $\mathbb{C}^n$, the n-dimensional complex Euclidean space, we denote by $P(X)$ the set of all continuous functions on X which can be uniformly approximated on X by polynomials in $z_1, \ldots ,z_n$. Here z_j denotes the j-th coordinate function on $\mathbb{C}^n$: $z_j(s_1, \ldots ,s_n) = s_j$.

Let X be a compact space, and $\mathcal{F}$ a subset of $C(X)$ which separates the points of X. The smallest closed subalgebra A of $C(X)$ which contains $\mathcal{F}$ and the constant functions is called the function algebra *generated* by $\mathcal{F}$; we also say that $\mathcal{F}$ is a *set of generators* for A. If $\mathcal{F}$ is a finite set, $\mathcal{F} = \{f_1, \ldots, f_n\}$, let $Y = \{(f_1(x), \ldots, f_n(x)) : x \in X\}$. Then Y is a compact subset of $\mathbb{C}^n$ homeomorphic to X, and A is isometrically isomorphic to $P(Y)$. Thus the study of finitely generated function algebras can be regarded as a branch of the theory of functions of several complex variables. This approach leads to some of the deepest and most interesting results in the subject. However, in this book we will not adopt this viewpoint, but limit ourselves to what can be learned by the methods of functional analysis.

If X is a compact subset of $\mathbb{C}^n$, we define $A(X)$ to be the set of all $f \in C(X)$ which are holomorphic in the interior of X, and $R(X)$ to be all those functions on X which are uniformly approximable by rational functions with no poles on X, i.e., by functions of the form p/q, where p and q are polynomials in the coordinate functions, and q has no zeroes on X. Evidently, $P(X) \subset R(X) \subset A(X)$. Each of the inclusions may be proper; we will study the situation in more detail in Chapter 3 for $n = 1$; for $n > 1$, the questions become much more difficult, and the subject remains in a primitive state.

The example that will serve as a touchstone throughout this volume is the following. Let $\Delta = \{s \in \mathbb{C} : |s| \leq 1\}$, the closed unit disk, and $\Gamma = \{s \in \mathbb{C} : |s| = 1\}$, the unit circle. We shall refer to $P(\Delta)$ as the *disk algebra on the disk*, to $P(\Gamma)$ as the *disk algebra on the circle*. We easily deduce from the maximum modulus principle that $P(\Delta)$ and $P(\Gamma)$ are isometrically isomorphic: this principle tells us that the restriction map of $C(\Delta)$ into $C(\Gamma)$ induces an isometry of $P(\Delta)$ into $P(\Gamma)$, and that a sequence of polynomials converging uniformly on Γ must necessarily converge uniformly on Δ, so this isometry is onto. It is easy to see that $P(\Delta) = A(\Delta)$. For if $f \in A(\Delta)$, put, for $0 < r < 1$, $f_r(\zeta) = f(r\zeta)$; then each f_r is holomorphic in a neighborhood of Δ, hence has a power series expansion converging uniformly on Δ, so $f_r \in P(\Delta)$; since $f_r \to f$ uniformly on Δ as $r \to 1$, it follows that $f \in P(\Delta)$. If $f \in C(\Gamma)$, we know from Fejer's theorem, or Weierstrass's, that f is uniformly approximable by polynomials in z and $\overline{z}$; since $\overline{z} = \frac{1}{z}$ on Γ, $f \in R(X)$. Thus $P(\Gamma) \subsetneq R(\Gamma) = C(\Gamma)$.

One obvious generalization of the disk algebra is the bicylinder algebra: let $\Gamma^2 = \Gamma \times \Gamma$, the two-dimensional torus in $\mathbb{C}^2$, $\Delta^2 = \Delta \times \Delta$, the closed unit bicylinder. It is easy to see that $P(\Delta^2)$ and $P(\Gamma^2)$ are isometrically isomorphic, by repeated applications of the maximum principle.

Another generalization of the disk algebra was first studied by Arens and Singer [2], and has had a great influence in the development of the subject. Let α be an irrational real number, and let A be the algebra on $\Gamma \times \Gamma$ generated by the functions $\{z_1{}^n z_2{}^m : n,m$ integers, $n + m\alpha \geq 0\}$. The elements of A were called "generalized analytic functions" by Arens and Singer; A is often referred to as the "big disk algebra". More generally, let G be a subgroup of the additive group of real numbers, regarded as a discrete topological group, and let $\hat{G}$ be its compact dual group. Each element $g \in G$ defines a continuous function of modulus 1 on $\hat{G}$ (in fact, a continuous homomorphism of $\hat{G}$ into Γ), which we denote by χ_g. The algebra A on $\hat{G}$ generated by $\{\chi_g : g \geq 0\}$ is also known as the algebra of generalized analytic functions, or the big disk algebra. If G is the group of integers, then $\hat{G} = \Gamma$, and A is exactly the disk algebra (on the circle). If $G = \{n + m\alpha : n,m \text{ integers}\}$ where α is irrational, then $\hat{G} = \Gamma \times \Gamma$, and we recover the big disk algebra first described, which might more properly be called the little big disk algebra. Further generalization is possible: G might be any ordered group, not necessarily a subgroup of the reals. We will not pursue the matter here.

Given a function algebra A on X, the most natural question to ask is: does $A = C(X)$? The fundamental theorem here is due to M. Stone, and is known as the Stone-Weierstrass theorem: $A = C(X)$ *if and only if the real functions in* A *separate the points of* X (or equivalently, if and only if $\bar{f} \in A$ whenever $f \in A$). This theorem by no means ends the discussion, however. For instance, we shall find in Chapter 3 that if X is a compact subset of $\mathbb{C}$, with empty interior and connected complement, then $R(X) = C(X)$; but there is usually no direct way to exhibit any non-constant real function in $R(X)$. Again, in cases where $A \neq C(X)$, it is not usual to prove this by exhibiting a function in A whose conjugate does not belong to A, or a pair of points in X not distinguished by any real function in A.

More generally, we can ask: if $A \neq C(X)$, or possibly with some stronger hypothesis, to what extent do the functions in A behave like holomorphic functions? I.e., to what extent is the disk algebra, for instance, prototypical? On the most superficial level, we observe for instance that there is a shortage of real functions among holomorphic functions, and this persists (Stone-Weierstrass) whenever $A \neq C(X)$. More interesting is the appearance of such phenomena as the Jensen inequality, Schwarz's lemma, and the maximum modulus principle, for instance, or the existence of point derivations, in situations of great generality; and it is especially interesting to deduce the presence of genuine analyticity from hypotheses of a general character, as we shall do in §4-4.

1-2 BANACH ALGEBRAS

DEFINITION: We call A a *normed algebra* if A has the structures of normed linear space and associative algebra over $\mathbb{C}$, and if

$\|fg\| \le \|f\|\|g\|$ for all $f,g \in A$. If A has a multiplicative unit, which we may denote by 1 without danger, we require also that $\|1\| = 1$. A *Banach algebra* is a complete normed algebra.

It is clear that a function algebra is a commutative Banach algebra with unit. Our interest in the more general category has two sources. Firstly, many theorems concerning function algebras have proofs that go over, word for word, to Banach algebras. Secondly, Banach algebras which are not function algebras may arise in the course of studying function algebras.

Here are some examples of Banach algebras which are not function algebras.

Let μ be a positive measure (non-negative extended-real valued countably additive function defined on a σ-algebra of subsets of some set). We recall that $L^\infty(\mu)$ is the set of equivalence classes of essentially bounded measurable functions, when f and g are called equivalent if $f = g$ almost everywhere (μ), and f is called essentially bounded if $\|f\| = \operatorname{esssup}|f| = \inf\{t : |f| \le t \text{ almost everywhere } (\mu)\} < \infty$.

With the pointwise operations and the essential sup norm, L^∞ is a commutative Banach algebra with unit.

Let Y be a set, and let $B(Y)$ be the set of all bounded complex valued functions on Y. With the pointwise operations and the sup norm, $B(Y)$ is a commutative Banach algebra with unit. This example is contained in the last one: $B(Y) = L^\infty(\mu)$, where μ is counting measure.

These two examples, as we shall see in the sequel, are merely function algebras in disguise but the disguise is only penetrated with the aid of some general Banach algebra theory. Here are two other examples, which are not realizeable as function algebras: let $C^{(n)}[0,1]$ be the space of n-times continuously differentiable functions on the closed unit interval. With the pointwise operations and the norm

$$\|f\| = \sum_0^n \frac{1}{K!} \sup\{|f^{(K)}(t)| : 0 \leq t \leq 1\},\ C^{(n)}[0,1]$$

is a commutative Banach algebra with unit, the prototype of a class extensively studied by Shilov (see Merkil [1]). Let Γ denote as before the unit circle, and let A be the algebra of all continuous functions on Γ which admit absolutely convergent Fourier series: $f \in A$ if and only if $f = \sum_{-\infty}^{\infty} c_n z^n$, where $\|f\| = \sum |c_n| < \infty$. With the pointwise operations and this norm, A is a commutative Banach algebra with unit, and its generalizations form the subject matter of harmonic analysis.

Banach algebras were introduced by Gelfand, in his fundamental paper of 1941 [1]. The main motivation for the study of Banach algebras was (and is) their applications to harmonic analysis, rather than uniform approximation. For these applications, and for more than the most elementary part of the general theory, which is all we describe here, see the books of Loomis, Naimark, or Rickart.

THEOREM 1.2.1. *Let* A *be a Banach algebra with unit. If* $f \in A$, $s \in \mathbb{C}$, *and* $\|f\| < |s|$, *then* $s - f$ *has an inverse, given by the norm-convergent series* $\sum_{0}^{\infty} \frac{f^n}{s^{n+1}}$.

Proof. Let $g = \frac{f}{s}$, so $\|g\| < 1$. The assertion of the theorem is that $1 - g$ has an inverse, given by $\sum_0^\infty g^n$. Let $G_n = \sum_0^n g^k$. Then for $m < n$, we have $\|G_n - G_m\| = \|\sum_{m+1}^n g^k\| \leq \sum_{m+1}^n \|g\|^k \leq \frac{\|g\|^{m+1}}{1 - \|g\|}$, by using the additive and multiplicative properties of the norm. Since $\|g\| < 1$, it follows that $\{G_n\}$ is a Cauchy sequence, and hence has a limit $G \in A$. Since $(1 - g)G_n = G_n(1 - g) = 1 - g^{n+1}$, and $g^{n+1} \to 0$ as we have seen, it follows that $(1 - g)G = G(1 - g) = 1$, which was to be proved.

We shall denote the set of invertible elements in an algebra with unit A by A^{-1}.

COROLLARY 1.2.2. *Let* A *be a Banach algebra with unit. Suppose* $f \in A^{-1}$, *and* $g \in A$, $\|f - g\| < \frac{1}{\|f^{-1}\|}$. *Then* $g \in A^{-1}$, *and*

$$\|f^{-1} - g^{-1}\| \leq \frac{\|f^{-1}\|^2 \|f - g\|}{1 - \|f^{-1}\| \|f - g\|} .$$

Proof. We have $\|1 - f^{-1}g\| \leq \|f^{-1}\| \|f - g\| < 1$, so $f^{-1}g$ has an inverse h. Multiplying the equation $f^{-1}gh = 1$ on the left and right by f and f^{-1} respectively, we find that $ghf^{-1} = 1$; since $hf^{-1}g = 1$, hf^{-1} is an inverse for g. Now

$$h = \sum_0^\infty (1 - f^{-1}g)^n = \sum_0^\infty [f^{-1}(f - g)]^n, \text{ and}$$

$$\|f^{-1} - g^{-1}\| = \|f^{-1} - hf^{-1}\|, \text{ so}$$

$$\begin{aligned}\|f^{-1} - g^{-1}\| &\leq \|1 - h\| \|f^{-1}\| \\ &\leq \|f^{-1}\| \sum_1^\infty \|f^{-1}\|^n \|f - g\|^n \\ &= \frac{\|f^{-1}\|^2 \|f - g\|}{1 - \|f^{-1}\| \|f - g\|},\end{aligned}$$

as was to be proved.

COROLLARY 1.2.3. *Let* A *be a Banach algebra with unit. Then* A^{-1} *is open, and the map* $f \to f^{-1}$ *is a homeomorphism of* A^{-1} *on itself.*

Proof. This is merely a qualitative statement of the more precise Corollary 1.2.2.

> Since the completion of a normed algebra is a Banach algebra, the estimate in 1.2.2 shows that the map $f \to f^{-1}$ is a continuous map (and therefore a homeomorphism) of A^{-1} onto itself for A a normed algebra; but A^{-1} need not be open if A is not complete.

DEFINITION. Let A be a normed algebra with unit, $f \in A$. We define spec f, the *spectrum* of f, by

$\operatorname{spec} f = \{s \in \mathbb{C} : s - f \notin A^{-1}\}$.

We observe that if A is a Banach algebra with unit, $f \in A$, then $\operatorname{spec} f$ is compact: for $\operatorname{spec} f$ is bounded by Theorem 1.2.1, and closed by Corollary 1.2.2.

Before going on with the general theory, we pause to give some non-trivial applications to some of the examples described in Section 1.

As an application of Theorem 1.2.1, we give here Paul Cohen's [2] proof of a famous result of Wermer, known as *Wermer's maximality theorem.*

THEOREM 1.2.4. *Let* A *be the disk algebra on the circle* Γ. *Let* B *be a closed subalgebra of* $C(\Gamma)$, *and suppose* $B \supset A$. *Then either* $B = A$ *or* $B = C(\Gamma)$.

Proof. Suppose there exists $f \in B$, $f \notin A$. Let $\sum_{-\infty}^{\infty} c_n z^n$ be the Fourier series of f. Then for some $n > 0$, $c_{-n} \neq 0$, else $f \in A$ by Fejér's theorem. Replacing f by $(c_{-n})^{-1} z^{n-1} f$, we can assume $c_{-1} = 1$. Then by Fejér's theorem, there exist polynomials g and h in z such that

$$zf = 1 + zg + \overline{zh} + k,$$

where $\|k\| < \frac{1}{2}$. Put $F = f - g - h$. Then $F \in B$, and $zF = 1 + \overline{zh} - zh + k \in B$. Since $zh - \overline{zh}$ is purely imaginary, we have $\|1 + t(zh - \overline{zh})\| \leq 1 + t^2\|zh - \overline{zh}\|^2$ for every real t. Hence

$$\begin{aligned} \|1 + t - tzF\| &= \|1 + t(zh - \overline{zh}) - tk\| \\ &\leq \|1 + t(zh - \overline{zh})\| + \|tk\| \\ &\leq 1 + t^2\|zh - \overline{zh}\| + t/2. \end{aligned}$$

Choosing $t > 0$ small enough, we then have $\|1 + t - tzF\| < 1 + t$, and hence by Theorem 1.2.1, $zF \in B^{-1}$, and hence $z^{-1} \in B$. It follows that $B = C(\Gamma)$, and the theorem is proved.

We shall give another proof of this theorem in the next chapter. Wermer's theorem initiated a spurt of research on the subject of maximality (see for instance Hoffman and Singer [1] and [3]). It has had some striking applications, which this volume is too small to contain. An earlier result found by Rudin is an immediate consequence of Theorem 1.2.4: *let* A *be a function algebra on* Δ, *with the properties:* $z \in A$, *and every function in* A *attains its maximum modulus on* Γ. *Then* A *is the disk algebra.*

We next use Theorem 1.2.1 to prove the following result: *if* X *is a compact subset of* $\mathbb{C}^n$, *then* R(X) *is generated by* n + 1 *functions.* For the proof, choose a sequence of polynomials $\{g_m\}$, such that each g_m has no zero on X and such that $\{\frac{p}{g_m} : p \text{ a polynomial}, m = 1,2, \ldots\}$ is dense in R(X). Now choose a sequence of positive constants $\{c_m\}$ with the properties:

$c_m\|\frac{1}{g_m}\| < 2^{-m}$ for every m, and $c_m\|\frac{g_k}{g_m}\| < 2^{-m}c_k$ whenever $1 \leq k < m$. The first condition assures us that $f = \sum_1^\infty \frac{c_k}{g_k} \in R(X)$; the second that $c_k > \sum_{k+1}^\infty c_m\|\frac{g_k}{g_m}\|$. Let A be the algebra generated by $z_1, \ldots, z_n$ and f. To show that A = R(X), it suffices to show that $\frac{1}{g_k} \in A$ for every k. Let $f_m = \sum_m^\infty \frac{c_k}{g_k}$. Then $f_1 = f \in A$, and if $\frac{1}{g_j} \in A$ for $j < m$, it follows that $f_m \in A$. We proceed by induction: if $f_m \in A$, then $f_m g_m \in A$, but $f_m g_m = c_m + \sum_{m+1}^\infty c_k \frac{g_m}{g_k}$, and $c_m > \|\sum_{m+1}^\infty c_k \frac{g_m}{g_k}\|$, so $f_m g_m \in A^{-1}$ by Theorem 1.2.1, whence $g_m^{-1} \in A$. This accomplishes the inductive step and completes the proof.

We now return to the general theory of Banach algebras.

THEOREM 1.2.5. *Let* A *be a Banach algebra with unit,* $f \in A$. *Then* spec f *is not empty.*

Proof. Suppose that spec f is empty, so that $s - f \in A^{-1}$ for every $s \in \mathbb{C}$. Let ϕ be any continuous linear functional on A, and put $F(s) = \phi((s - f)^{-1})$ for each $s \in \mathbb{C}$. Since $(s - f)^{-1} - (t - f)^{-1} = (t - s)(s - f)^{-1}(t - f)^{-1}$ for all $s, t \in \mathbb{C}$, as can be seen by multiplying both sides by $(t - f)(s - f)$, we have $\frac{F(s) - F(t)}{s - t} = -\phi[(s - f)^{-1}(t - f)^{-1}]$. It follows from Corollary 1.2.3 that F is entire, and $F'(s) = -\phi((s - f)^{-2})$ for all $s \in \mathbb{C}$. Since $(s - f)^{-1} = s^{-1}(1 - s^{-1}f)^{-1}$, and $(1 - s^{-1}f)^{-1} \to 1$ as $s \to \infty$ by Corollary 1.2.3, $F(s) \to 0$ as $s \to \infty$. But an entire function which vanishes at ∞ must be identically zero, by Liouville's theorem. Thus

$\phi((s - f)^{-1}) = 0$ for all s. Since ϕ was an arbitrary linear functional, it follows that $(s - f)^{-1} = 0$, for all s. But this is impossible for any s, and this contradiction proves the theorem.

> Since the completion of a normed algebra is a Banach algebra, it follows that spec f is not empty for any f in any normed algebra with unit.

COROLLARY 1.2.6. *A normed algebra with the property* $A^{-1} = A\backslash\{0\}$ *is one-dimensional.*

<u>Proof</u>. If $f \in A$, there exists $s \in \mathbb{C}$, by Theorem 1.2.5, such that $(s - f) \notin A^{-1}$. By hypothesis, this implies $f = s$.

> This result is known as the Gelfand-Mazur theorem.

LEMMA 1.2.7. *Let* A *be a Banach algebra with unit,* $f \in A$. *Then* $s \in \text{spec } f^n$ *if and only if* $s = t^n$ *for some* $t \in \text{spec } f$.

<u>Proof</u>. Let $t_1, \ldots, t_n$ be the n-th roots of s. Then $f^n - s = (f - t_1)\cdots(f - t_n)$, and it is clear that $f^n - s$ fails to be invertible if and only if

$f - t_j$ fails to be invertible for some j, which is the assertion of the Lemma.

We combine this lemma with a refinement of the argument used in Theorem 1.2.5 to prove a quantitative version of this theorem, known as the *spectral radius formula.*

THEOREM 1.2.8. *Let* A *be a Banach algebra with unit,* $f \in A$. *Then*

$$\sup\{|s| : s \in \operatorname{spec} f\} = \lim_{n\to\infty} \|f^n\|^{1/n}.$$

<u>Proof</u>. Let $s \in \operatorname{spec} f$. By Lemma 1.2.7, $s^n \in \operatorname{spec} f^n$, and by Theorem 1.2.1 it follows that $|s^n| \leq \|f^n\|$ for every positive integer n, i.e., $|s| \leq \|f^n\|^{1/n}$ for all n, so $|s| \leq \inf\|f^n\|^{1/n}$. Let $R = \sup\{|s| : s \in \operatorname{spec} f\}$. For each continuous linear functional ϕ on A, put $F(s) = \phi((s - f)^{-1})$; as we observed in the proof of Theorem 1.2.5, F is holomorphic in $\mathbb{C}\setminus\operatorname{spec} f$, hence in $\{s \in \mathbb{C} : |s| > R\}$. Since (Theorem 1.2.1)

$$F(s) = \sum_{0}^{\infty} \frac{\phi(f^n)}{s^{n+1}}$$

for $|s| > \|f\|$, it follows from the elements of complex function theory that the series converges for $|s| > R$. In particular, $\{\phi(\frac{f^n}{s^n})\}$ is a bounded sequence for any $\phi \in A^*$, $|s| > R$. By the Banach-Steinhaus theorem (uniform boundedness principle), it follows that $\frac{f^n}{s^n}$ is a bounded sequence in A, for $|s| > R$. Thus, if $|s| > R$, there exists a constant K such that $\|f^n\| \leq K|s|^n$, for all n, and hence $\limsup\|f^n\|^{1/n} \leq |s|$. Thus $\limsup\|f^n\|^{1/n} \leq R \leq \inf\|f^n\|^{1/n}$, and the theorem is proved.

DEFINITION. Let A be a Banach algebra with unit. We say that ϕ is a *multiplicative linear functional* on A if ϕ is a non-zero linear functional on A, such that $\phi(fg) = \phi(f)\phi(g)$ for every $f,g \in A$; i.e., if ϕ is a homomorphism of A onto $\mathbb{C}$. We denote the set of all multiplicative linear functionals on A by Spec A.

It is obvious that if $\phi \in$ Spec A, then $\phi(1) = 1$, and for $f \in A^{-1}$, $\phi(f^{-1}) = (\phi(f))^{-1}$; in particular, $\phi(f) \neq 0$ for all $f \in A^{-1}$.

LEMMA 1.2.9. *Let* $\phi \in \operatorname{Spec} A$. *Then* ϕ *is a continuous linear functional, and* $\|\phi\| = 1$.

<u>Proof</u>. Let $f \in A$. Then $s - f \in A^{-1}$ for any s, $|s| > \|f\|$, by Theorem 1.2.1, so $\phi(s - f) \neq 0$, i.e., $\phi(f) \neq s$. Thus $|\phi(f)| \leq \|f\|$, for any $f \in A$, which was to be proved.

DEFINITION. Let A be a Banach algebra with unit. For each $f \in A$, we define the *Gelfand transform* $\hat{f}$ of f, $\hat{f} : \operatorname{Spec} A \to \mathbb{C}$, by $\hat{f}(\phi) = \phi(f)$ for $\phi \in \operatorname{Spec} A$. We define the *Gelfand topology* on $\operatorname{Spec} A$ to be the weak $\hat{A}$ topology, i.e., the weakest topology on $\operatorname{Spec} A$ for which all the functions $\hat{f}(f \in A)$ are continuous.

Lemma 1.2.9 shows that $\operatorname{Spec} A$ is a subset of the closed unit ball of A^*. We observe that the map $f \to \hat{f}$ consists of the canonical injection of A into A^{**}, followed by restriction to $\operatorname{Spec} A$. The Gelfand topology on $\operatorname{Spec} A$ is the relative weak-* topology. Since $\{\phi \in A^* : \phi(fg) = \phi(f)\phi(g)\}$ is weak-* closed for each $f,g \in A$, and $\operatorname{Spec} A$ is the intersection of all such sets with the hyperplane $\{\phi \in A^* : \phi(1) = 1\}$, we see that $\operatorname{Spec} A$

is a weak-* closed subset of the closed unit ball in A^*, and hence Spec A is compact, with the Gelfand topology. Thus, $\hat{A} = \{\hat{f} : f \in A\}$ is a separating algebra of functions on the compact Hausdorff space Spec A. The homomorphism $f \to \hat{f}$ of A into C(Spec A) is called the *Gelfand representation of* A.

If A is a function algebra on X, the Gelfand representation has a simple interpretation. For each $x \in X$, let $\tau_x(f) = f(x)$ for all $f \in A$. It is obvious that $\tau_x \in \text{Spec } A$. The map $\tau : X \to \text{Spec } A$ is one-to-one, since A separates the points of X, and continuous by a remark we made immediately following the definition of function algebra. Thus τ is a homeomorphism of X onto a closed subset of Spec A, and $\hat{f} \circ \tau = f$ for each $f \in A$. Thus we may regard X as a closed subset of Spec A, and f as the restriction of $\hat{f}$ to X. The Gelfand representation, which is always norm-decreasing by Lemma 1.2.9, is seen in this case to be an isometry: each $\hat{f} \in \hat{A}$ takes its maximum modulus on $\tau(X)$, this maximum being $\|f\|$. Thus we may view Spec A as the largest compact space to which the functions in A may be extended so as to form a function algebra. The example to keep in mind is the disk algebra on the circle, which can be extended to form the disk algebra on the disk.

Let A be a commutative Banach algebra with unit. We say that I is an *ideal* in A if I is a linear subspace of A and $fg \in I$ whenever $f \in A$ and $g \in I$. An ideal I is called *proper* if $I \neq A$, or equivalently, if $1 \notin I$; A is called the *unit ideal*. A *maximal ideal* is a proper ideal not properly contained in any proper ideal.

LEMMA 1.2.10. *If* A *is a commutative algebra with unit, and* I *a proper ideal in* A*, then* $I \subset M$ *for some maximal ideal* M.

Proof. Let $\mathcal{A}$ be the collection of all proper ideals containing I. Order $\mathcal{A}$ by inclusion. If $\mathcal{S}$ is a linearly ordered subcollection of $\mathcal{A}$, then $\cup\{J : J \in \mathcal{S}\}$ is clearly an ideal, and proper since $1 \notin J$ for each $J \in \mathcal{S}$. The lemma now follows from Zorn's lemma.

LEMMA 1.2.11. *Let* A *be a commutative Banach algebra with unit,* I *a proper ideal in* A. *Then the closure* $\overline{I}$ *of* I *is a proper ideal. In particular, every maximal ideal is closed.*

Proof. That $\overline{I}$ is an ideal is trivial. If I is proper, then no $f \in I$ is invertible; it follows from Theorem 1.2.1 that $\|1 - f\| \geq 1$ for all $f \in I$, and hence for all $f \in \overline{I}$. Hence $1 \notin \overline{I}$, and the lemma is proved.

We recall that if I is a linear subspace of a linear space A, the *quotient space* A/I is the set of cosets of I, i.e., the set of equivalence classes under the relation: $f \sim g$ if and only if $f - g \in I$. Denote the canonical map of A onto A/I by π. It is trivial to verify that if $f \sim h$ and $g \sim k$, then $f + g \sim h + k$, and $sf \sim sh$ for any $s \in C$; thus A/I has the structure of linear space. If A is a commutative algebra, and I is an ideal in A, it is trivial that also $fg \sim hk$, so A/I is a commutative algebra. If A has a unit, then $\pi 1$ is a unit for A/I. It is clear that π is a homomorphism. If A is a normed linear space, and I a closed subspace, then A/I is a normed linear space with the *quotient norm* $\|\pi f\| = \inf\{\|g\| : \pi g = \pi f\}$. If A is a normed algebra, it is trivial to verify that $\|(\pi f)(\pi g)\| \leq \|\pi f\|\|\pi g\|$, so A/I is a normed algebra if A is, and I is a closed ideal in A. If A is a Banach space, and I a closed subspace, it is well known that A/I is a Banach space. If A is a commutative Banach algebra with unit, and I a proper closed ideal, we have then that A/I is a commutative Banach algebra with unit, for $\|\pi 1\| = 1$ by Theorem 1.2.1.

Let X be a compact Hausdorff space, K a closed subset of X, $I = \{f \in C(X) : f = 0$ on $K\}$. Clearly I is a closed ideal in C(X). The reader may verify that C(X)/I is naturally isomorphic to C(K).

If A is a function algebra, and I a closed ideal in A, the Banach algebra A/I need not be realizeable as a function algebra. For example, if A is the disk algebra, and $I = \{f \in A : f(0) = f'(0) = 0\}$, one easily verifies that A/I is a two-dimensional algebra, with basis $\{1, \pi z\}$, and $(\pi z)^2 = 0$ (of course, in a function algebra, $f^2 = 0$ only if $f = 0$).

THEOREM 1.2.12. *Let* A *be a commutative Banach algebra with unit. If* $\phi \in \operatorname{Spec} A$, *then* $\ker \phi$ *is a maximal ideal in* A. *If* M *is a maximal ideal in* A, *then* $M = \ker \phi$ *for some* $\phi \in \operatorname{Spec} A$. (Here, $\ker \phi$ denotes the kernel of ϕ, i.e., $\{f \in A : \phi(f) = 0\}$.)

Proof. If $\phi(f) = 0$ and $g \in A$, then $\phi(fg) = 0$, so $\ker \phi$ is an ideal; since $\phi(1) = 1$, $\ker \phi$ is proper; it is maximal since it has codimension 1 (if $g \notin \ker \phi$, we may write, for any $f \in A$, $f = (f - cg) + cg$, where $c = \phi(f)/\phi(g)$; thus g and $\ker \phi$ generate the unit ideal).

If M is a maximal ideal in A, then A/M is a Banach algebra with unit. If I is an ideal in A/M, then $\pi^{-1}(I)$ is an ideal in A containing M, hence either M or A. Thus $\{0\}$ is the only proper ideal in A/M. It follows that if $f \in A/M$, $f \neq 0$, then $f \in (A/M)^{-1}$, and by the Gelfand-Mazur theorem (Corollary 1.2.6) it follows that A/M is one-dimensional. Thus, for each $f \in A$, there is a uniquely determined $\phi(f) \in \mathbb{C}$ such that $f - \phi(f) \in M$. It is clear that $\phi \in \operatorname{Spec} A$ and $\ker \phi = M$, and the proof is concluded.

COROLLARY 1.2.13. *Let* A *be a commutative Banach algebra with unit, and let* $f_1, \ldots, f_n \in A$. *Then either there exists* $\phi \in \text{Spec } A$ *such that* $\phi(f_j) = 0$ $(1 \le j \le n)$, *or else there exist* $g_1, \ldots, g_n \in A$ *such that* $\sum f_j g_j = 1$. *In particular,* $f \in A^{-1}$ *if and only if* $\phi(f) \neq 0$ *for every* $\phi \in \text{Spec } A$.

Proof. Let $I = \{\sum f_j g_j : g_j \in A, 1 \le j \le n\}$, the ideal generated by $f_1, \ldots, f_n$. If I is a proper ideal, it is contained in a maximal ideal by Lemma 1.2.10, and so $I \subset \ker \phi$ for some $\phi \in \text{Spec } A$ by Theorem 1.2.12. If I is not proper, then $1 \in I$. The Corollary is proved.

COROLLARY 1.2.14. *For every* $f \in A$, $\text{spec } f = \hat{f}(\text{Spec } A)$. *Hence* $\|\hat{f}\| = \lim \|f^n\|^{1/n}$.

Proof. $s \in \text{spec } f$ if and only if $s - f \notin A^{-1}$, if and only if there exists $\phi \in \text{Spec } A$ with $0 = \phi(s - f) = s - \phi(f) = s - \hat{f}(\phi)$. The other assertion is now a consequence of Theorem 1.2.8.

In view of Theorem 1.2.12, we shall refer to Spec A, when A is a commutative Banach algebra with unit, as the *maximal ideal space* of A.

The spectral radius formula gives an answer to the question: *when is the Gelfand transform an isometry*, or in other words, *when is* A *a disguised function algebra*? The answer: *if and only if* $\|f\|^2 = \|f^2\|$ *for every* $f \in A$. Similarly, it gives a description of the kernel of the Gelfand transform: $\hat{f} = 0$ if and only if $\lim \|f^n\|^{1/n} = 0$, i.e., if and only if f is a *generalized nilpotent*. A commutative Banach algebra with unit A is called *semi-simple* if and only if the Gelfand transform is an isomorphism, i.e., if and only if the intersection of all the maximal ideal of A (the so-called *radical*) is $\{0\}$, i.e., if and only if A possesses no non-zero generalized nilpotents.

1-3 THE MAXIMAL IDEAL SPACES OF SOME EXAMPLES

THEOREM 1.3.1. *Let* X *be a compact Hausdorff space. Then* Spec $C(X) = X$, i.e., *for every* $\phi \in$ Spec $C(X)$ *there exists* $x \in X$ *such that* $\phi(f) = f(x)$ *for every* $f \in C(X)$.

Proof. It suffices to show that all the functions in $\ker \phi$ have a common zero $x \in X$, for then $\ker \phi \subset \ker \tau_x$ (recall that τ_x is the evaluation functional at x), so $\tau_x = c\phi$ for some $c \in \mathbb{C}$, and since $\phi(1) = \tau_x(1) = 1$, it follows that $\phi = \tau_x$. Let $\{f_1, \dots, f_n\}$ be a finite subset of $\ker \phi$. If $f_1, \dots, f_n$ have no common zero, then $p = \sum f_j \overline{f}_j$ is strictly positive on X, so $p^{-1} \in C(X)$, so $0 \neq \phi(p) = \sum \phi(f_j)\phi(\overline{f}_j) = 0$. This contradiction shows that every finite subset of $\ker \phi$ has a common zero. It follows from the finite intersection principle that all the functions in $\ker \phi$ have a common zero, concluding the proof.

Given two compact Hausdorff spaces X and Y, when are $C(X)$ and $C(Y)$ isomorphic algebras? Clearly, if X and Y are homeomorphic, the map $T : C(X) \to C(Y)$ given by $Tf = f \circ \eta$, where η is a homeomorphism of Y onto X, is an isomorphism onto. Conversely, Theorem 1.3.1 shows that every isomorphism of $C(X)$ onto $C(Y)$ is of this form. For if T an isomorphism of $C(X)$ onto $C(Y)$, then for each $y \in Y$ the map $f \to (Tf)(y)$ is a multiplicative linear functional on $C(X)$, hence there exists $\eta(y) \in X$ such that $Tf(y) = f(\eta(y))$ for all $f \in C(X)$. It is easy to check that η is a homeomorphism of Y onto X.

THEOREM 1.3.2 *Let* X *be a topological space, and let* A *be the Banach algebra (with pointwise operations and the sup norm) of all bounded continuous functions on* X. *Then the Gelfand representation is an isometry of* A *onto* $C(\text{Spec } A)$.

Proof. Since $\|f^n\| = \|f\|^n$ for every $f \in A$, every positive integer n, it follows from the spectral radius formula that the Gelfand map is an isometry. If $f \in A$ is real-valued, then for every $s \in \mathbb{C}$ with $\operatorname{Im} s \neq 0$, $f - s \in A^{-1}$; hence $\hat{f} - s$ does not vanish on Spec A; it follows that $\hat{f}$ is real-valued. Hence $(\overline{f})^\wedge = (\hat{f})^-$ for every $f \in A$. Thus $\hat{A}$ is closed under complex conjugation, and it follows from the Stone-Weierstrass theorem that $\hat{A} = C(\text{Spec } A)$.

Recall that a topological space X is called *completely regular* if for every closed subset F of X and any $x \in X \setminus F$ there exists a continuous function f on X with $0 \leq f \leq 1$, $f(x) = 1$, and $f = 0$ on F. A subspace of a compact Hausdorff space is completely regular, by Urysohn's Lemma.

THEOREM 1.3.3. *Let* X *be a completely regular space. Then there exists a compact Hausdorff space* $\tilde{X}$*, called the* Stone-Cech compactification *of* X*, with the following properties:*

i) *there exists an imbedding* τ *of* X *onto a dense subspace of* $\tilde{X}$*;*

ii) $\tilde{X}$ *is a maximal "compactification" of* X*, in the sense that if* Y *is a compact Hausdorff space, and* τ' *a continuous map of* X *onto a dense subspace of* Y*, then there exists a continuous map* Φ *of* $\tilde{X}$ *onto* Y*, such that* $\tau' = \Phi \circ \tau$.

Proof. We take $\tilde{X} = \text{Spec } A$, where A is the algebra of all bounded continuous functions on X, and define τ by $\tau(x)(f) = f(x)$ for all $f \in A$. From the hypothesis that X is completely regular, it follows easily that τ is a homeomorphism of

X onto $\tau(X)$. We now observe that $\tau(X)$ is dense; for suppose $g \in C(\tilde{X})$ vanishes on $\tau(X)$. By Theorem 1.3.2, $g = \hat{f}$ for some $f \in A$. But then $f(x) = \hat{f}(\tau(x)) = 0$ for every $x \in X$, i.e., $f = 0$, so $\hat{f} = 0$; thus every $g \in C(\tilde{X})$ which vanishes on $\tau(X)$ must vanish identically, so $\tau(X)$ is dense in $\tilde{X}$. Now suppose τ' is a continuous map of X onto a dense subspace of the compact Hausdorff space Y. Then $f \circ \tau' \in A$ whenever $f \in C(Y)$, so the map $f \to (f \circ \tau')^{\wedge}(\tilde{x})$ is a multiplicative linear functional on $C(Y)$ for every $\tilde{x} \in \tilde{X}$. Applying Theorem 3.1.1, we find for each $\tilde{x} \in \tilde{X}$ there exists $\Phi(\tilde{x}) \in Y$ such that $(f \circ \tau')^{\wedge}(\tilde{x}) = f(\Phi(\tilde{x}))$ for every $f \in C(Y)$. In particular, taking $\tilde{x} = \tau(x)$ for $x \in X$, we have $f(\tau'(x)) = f(\Phi \circ \tau(x))$ for every $f \in C(Y)$, so $\tau' = \Phi \circ \tau$. It is easy to see that Φ is continuous. Since $\Phi(X) \supset \tau'(X)$, $\tau'(X)$ is dense, and $\Phi(\tilde{X})$ is compact, it follows that Φ maps $\tilde{X}$ onto Y. The proof is finished.

THEOREM 1.3.4. *Let* μ *be a positive measure. Then there exists a totally disconnected compact*

Hausdorff space X *and an order-preserving isometric isomorphism of* $L^\infty(\mu)$ *onto* C(X).

<u>Proof</u>. We take $X = \text{Spec } L^\infty(\mu)$, and show that the Gelfand representation has the properties listed. Since $\|f^n\| = \|f\|^n$ for every $f \in L^\infty(\mu)$ and every positive integer n, it follows from the spectral radius formula that the Gelfand representation is an isometry. We call an element $f \in L^\infty(\mu)$ *real-valued* if some (and hence every) representative of f is real almost everywhere (μ). If $f \in L^\infty(\mu)$ is real-valued, then $f - s \in L^\infty(\mu)^{-1}$ whenever $s \in \mathbb{C}$, Im $s \neq 0$, whence $\hat{f} - s$ has no zeroes on X when Im $s \neq 0$, and thus $\hat{f}$ is real-valued. It follows that $(\overline{f})^\wedge = (\hat{f})^-$ for every $f \in L^\infty(\mu)$, so the algebra of Gelfand transforms is closed under complex conjugation, and hence equals C(X). If $f \in L^\infty(\mu)$ and $f \geq 0$, then $f = g^2$ for some real-valued $g \in L^\infty(\mu)$, so $\hat{f} = \hat{g}^2 \geq 0$: the Gelfand representation is order-preserving. If $f = \chi_E$, the characteristic function of a μ-measurable set E, then $f^2 = f$, so $\hat{f}^2 = \hat{f}$; if we put $\hat{E} = \{x \in X : \hat{f}(x) = 1\}$, it follows that $\hat{f} = \chi_{\hat{E}}$. Since $\hat{f}$ is continuous, $\hat{E}$

must be both open and closed. Since finite linear combinations of such χ_E are dense in $L^\infty(\mu)$, it follows that linear combinations of the characteristic functions of open-and-closed subsets of X are uniformly dense in C(X), which is easily seen to be equivalent to X being totally disconnected. All is proven.

If Y is any set, the algebra B(Y) of all bounded functions on Y is isometrically isomorphic to C(X), where X may be regarded as either the Stone-Cech compactification of Y with the discrete topology, or the maximal ideal space of $L^\infty(\mu)$, where μ is counting measure on Y.

Let U be the open unit disk in the complex plane, and let $H^\infty(U)$ be the algebra of all bounded holomorphic functions on U. The maximal ideal space of $H^\infty(U)$ is an extremely complicated object, extensively studied (see especially Hoffman [3]). The map $s \to$ (evaluation at s) is easily seen to imbed U as an open subset of Spec $H^\infty(U)$. It is a deep theorem of Carleson [1] that the image of U under this map is dense in Spec $H^\infty(U)$.

Let σ be Lebesgue measure on the circle Γ, and let $H^\infty(\sigma)$ be the weak-* closure in $L^\infty(\sigma)$ of the disk algebra on Γ. The algebras $H^\infty(U)$ and $H^\infty(\sigma)$ are identified by means of a classical theorem of Fatou, which states: *let* $f \in H^\infty(U)$; *then for almost all* $s \in \Gamma$, $f^*(s) = \lim_{r\to 1} f(rs)$ *exists;* $f^* \in H^\infty(\sigma)$; *for every* $g \in H^\infty(\sigma)$, *there exists* $f \in H^\infty(U)$ *(given by the Cauchy integral formula) such that* $f^* = g$ *almost everywhere*. Via the Gelfand representation, $H^\infty(\sigma)$ may be regarded as a closed subalgebra of $C(X)$, where X is the maximal ideal space of $L^\infty(\sigma)$. We shall discuss $H^\infty(\sigma)$ again in Chapter 4, and find that $H^\infty(\sigma)$ separates the points of X (so that it is a function algebra on X).

It is easily seen that if A is the disk algebra, Spec A can be identified with the closed disk Δ. For if $\phi \in$ Spec A, and we put $s = \phi(z)$, we have $s \in \Delta$ since $|\phi(z)| \leq \|z\| = 1$. If f is a polynomial in z, then so is $g = \dfrac{f - f(s)}{z - s}$. Hence $\phi(f) = \phi[f(s) + (z - s)g] = f(s) + (\phi(z) - s)\phi(g) = f(s)$ for all polynomials f, and hence for all $f \in A$. On the other hand, for each $s \in \Delta$, the map $f \to f(s)$ clearly belongs to Spec A. Thus $\hat{z}$ maps Spec A homeomorphically onto Δ. This remark can be generalized.

DEFINITION. Let A be a commutative Banach algebra with unit, and $f_1, \ldots, f_n \in A$. The *joint spectrum* of $f_1, \ldots, f_n$ is defined by

$$\operatorname{spec}(f_1, \ldots, f_n) = \{(\hat{f}_1(\phi), \ldots, \hat{f}_n(\phi)) : \phi \in \operatorname{Spec} A\}.$$

Thus, $\operatorname{spec}(f_1, \ldots, f_n)$ is a compact subset of $\mathbb{C}^n$; if $n = 1$, this notion agrees with the other definition by Corollary 1.2.14.

DEFINITION. If A is a Banach algebra with unit, and S a subset of A, by the *algebra generated by* S we mean the smallest closed subalgebra B (with unit) of A such that $B \supset S$. We call S a *set of generators* for B.

If $\{f_1, \ldots, f_n\}$ is a set of generators for A, it is clear that $\{\hat{f}_1, \ldots, \hat{f}_n\}$ separates the points of Spec A. Thus the map

$\phi \to (\hat{f}_1(\phi), \ldots, \hat{f}_n(\phi))$ is a homeomorphism of Spec A onto $\mathrm{spec}(f_1, \ldots, f_n)$.

Let A be the algebra of functions with absolutely convergent Fourier series, introduced on pp. 10-11. We leave to the reader the verification that Spec A may be identified with the circle Γ, the Gelfand representation being the identity. Applying Corollary 1.2.13, we then find the classical theorem of Wiener: *if* $f_1, \ldots, f_n$ *are continuous functions on* Γ *with absolutely convergent Fourier series and no common zero, then there exist* $g_1, \ldots, g_n$ *with absolutely convergent Fourier series such that* $\sum f_j g_j = 1$. This result is not easy to prove by direct arguments, even for $n = 1$ (in fact, using the argument in the proof of Theorem 1.3.1, the general case follows immediately from the case $n = 1$). Similarly, Corollary 1.2.13 tells us that if $f_1, \ldots, f_n$ are functions in the disk algebra with no common zero on Δ, then there exist $g_1, \ldots, g_n$ in the disk algebra such that $\sum f_j g_j = 1$. This result, obvious for $n = 1$, is not easy to prove in general without recourse to the Gelfand theory. Carleson's theorem, referred to above, has the formulation: *if* $f_1, \ldots, f_n$ *are bounded holomorphic functions on the open disk* U, *and* $\sum|f_j|$ *is bounded away from zero on* U, *then there exist bounded holomorphic* $g_1, \ldots, g_n$ *on* U *with* $\sum f_j g_j = 1$. This is easily seen to be equivalent to the formulation: U is dense in $\text{Spec } H^\infty(U)$.

DEFINITION. Let K be a compact subset of $\mathbb{C}^n$. We define $\hat{K}$, the *polynomial convex hull of* K, by

$$\hat{K} = \{s \in \mathbb{C}^n : |p(s)| \leq \|p\|_K \text{ for every polynomial } p\}$$

It is obvious that $\hat{K}$ is a compact subset of $\mathbb{C}^n$ containing K, and that the restriction map of $C(\hat{K})$ onto $C(K)$ induces an isometry of $P(\hat{K})$ onto $P(K)$.

THEOREM 1.3.5. *Let* A *be a commutative Banach algebra with unit, generated by* $f_1, \ldots, f_n$. *Let* X *be a closed subset of* $\text{Spec } A$ *with the property: for each* $f \in A$, $\|\hat{f}\| = \|\hat{f}\|_X$. *Let* $K = \{(\hat{f}_1(\phi), \ldots, \hat{f}_n(\phi)) : \phi \in X\}$. *Then*

$\hat{K} = \text{spec}(f_1, \ldots, f_n)$.

Proof. Let $s \in \hat{K}$. Then for every polynomial p,

$$|p(s)| \leq \|p\|_K = \|p(\hat{f}_1, \ldots, \hat{f}_n)\|_X = \|p(f_1, \ldots, f_n)^\wedge\| \leq \|p(f_1, \ldots, f_n)\|.$$

Thus, the map $p(f_1, \ldots, f_n) \to p(s)$, which is obviously a multiplicative linear functional on the algebra of all polynomials in $f_1, \ldots, f_n$, is bounded, and hence extends to a multiplicative linear functional on A. Thus $s = (\hat{f}_1(\phi), \ldots, \hat{f}_n(\phi))$ for some $\phi \in \text{Spec } A$ whenever $s \in \hat{K}$, i.e., $\hat{K} \subset \text{spec}(f_1, \ldots, f_n)$.

On the other hand, if $s \in \text{spec}(f_1, \ldots, f_n)$, then for every polynomial p, we have

$$|p(s)| = |p(\hat{f}_1(\phi), \ldots, \hat{f}_n(\phi)| = |p(\hat{f}_1, \ldots, \hat{f}_n)(\phi)| \leq \|p(\hat{f}_1, \ldots, \hat{f}_n\| = \|p(\hat{f}_1, \ldots, \hat{f}_n\|_X = \|p(z_1, \ldots, z_n)\|_K,$$

so $s \in \hat{K}$. This concludes the proof.

COROLLARY 1.3.6 *If* X *is a compact set in* $\mathbb{C}^n$, *then* $\text{Spec } P(X) = \hat{X}$ *(with the usual identification of points with the associated evaluation homomor-*

phisms).

We call a compact set X in $\mathbb{C}^n$ *polynomially convex* if $\hat{X} = X$. We see from the last corollary, and Theorem 1.3.1, that *a necessary condition that* $P(X) = C(X)$ *is that* X *be polynomially convex.*

If X is a compact subset of $\mathbb{C}$, $\hat{X}$ is easy to determine. From the maximum modulus principle, it follows at once that $\hat{X}$ contains, along with X, every bounded component of $\mathbb{C}\backslash X$. We can see that $\hat{X}$ contains nothing else, as follows. If $s \notin \hat{X}$, then $f = (z - s)^{-1} \in P(X)$, in view of the identification of $\hat{X} = \text{spec } z$. Let $\delta = |s - X|$, the distance from s to X. If $|t - s| < \delta/2$, we have $|f(t)| > \frac{2}{\delta}$, while $\|f\| = \frac{1}{\delta}$, and thus $t \notin \hat{X}$. Now if s is in the unbounded component of $\mathbb{C}\backslash X$, we can choose a finite set $s_0, \ldots, s_n$ such that $s = s_0$, $|s_n| > \|z\|_X$, and $|s_k - s_{k-1}| < \frac{1}{2}|s_k - X|$ for $k = 1, \ldots, n$. Since $s_n \notin \hat{X} = \text{spec } z$ (Theorem 1.2.1), applying the argument above repeatedly, we arrive at $s \notin \hat{X}$. Thus $\hat{X}$ *is the union of* X *and its bounded com-*

plementary components; X *is polynomially convex if and only if it has connected complement.* Thus in order that $P(X) = C(X)$, it is necessary that X have connected complement and empty interior. It is a theorem of Lavrentiev that these conditions are in fact sufficient; we shall obtain this result in Chapter 3.

When $n > 1$, the problem of finding $\hat{X}$, or even of determining if X is polynomially convex, is much more difficult, and has only been solved for special cases. Again, $\hat{X}$ must contain every bounded component of the complement of X (in fact, when $n > 1$, much more is true: a theorem of Hartogs states that every function holomorphic in a neighborhood of X extends to a function holomorphic in every bounded complementary component). Even more is true: if R is a finite bordered Riemann surface holomorphically imbedded in $\mathbb{C}^n$, and $\partial R \subset X$, then $R \subset \hat{X}$ by the maximum modulus principle. One might conjecture that if X contains such an R whenever $X \supset \partial R$, then X is polynomially convex. But Stolzenberg [1] has given an ingenious counter-example. It is known that if the compact set $X \subset \mathbb{C}$ has connected complement, then so does any homeomorphic image of X in $\mathbb{C}$. Thus polynomial convexity is a purely topological property for plane sets. This is no longer true in higher dimensions: consider the circles $X_1 = \{s \in \mathbb{C}^2 : |s_1| = 1, s_2 = 0\}$, and $X_2 = \{s \in \mathbb{C}^2 : |s_1| = 1, s_1 s_2 = 1\}$. It is easy to see that $\hat{X}_1 = \{s \in \mathbb{C}^2 : |s_1| \leq 1, s_2 = 0\}$, while X_2 is polynomially convex ($P(X_1)$ is the disk algebra, while $P(X_2) = C(X_2)$).

It can be shown quite easily that compact convex sets in $\mathbb{C}^n$ are polynomially convex, and it is not hard to show that the union of two disjoint convex compact sets is also polynomially convex. Need the union of *three* disjoint compact convex sets be polynomially convex? This question, apparently first raised by the German school of several complex variables in the early 30's, was only answered in 1965, by Kallin [2]. She showed that the answer is *yes*, for disjoint closed balls, but *no*, for polycylinders.

To study the maximal ideal space of $R(X)$, we introduce the following:

DEFINITION. Let X be a compact set in $\mathbb{C}^n$. The *rational convex hull* of X is the set $\hat{X}_R$ of all $s \in \mathbb{C}^n$ with the property: there exists no polynomial p such that $p(s) = 0$ while p has no zeroes on X.

It is trivial that the rational convex hull of X is a compact set containing X. We call X *rationally convex* if it coincides with its rational convex hull. It is obvious that every compact set in $\mathbb{C}$ is rationally convex. From the definition of $\hat{X}_R$ we see that if $s \in \hat{X}_R$, $f(s)$ is well-defined for every rational function f with no poles on X; further, $|f(s)| \leq \|f\|_X$ for all such functions f. For if $|f(s)| > \|f\|_X$, and $f = p/q$, where p and q are polynomials and $q \neq 0$ on X, we see that $p - f(s)q$ is a polynomial which vanishes at s, but at no point of X. This shows that each point of $\hat{X}_R$ defines an element of Spec $R(X)$. On the other hand, if $\phi \in \text{Spec } R(X)$, let $s = (\phi(z_1,), \ldots ,\phi(z_n))$. Then $\phi(p) = p(s)$ for any polynomial p; if q a polynomial with no zeroes on X, $q^{-1} \in R(X)$, so $\phi(p/q) = \phi(p)/\phi(q) = \frac{p}{q}(s)$; thus ϕ is determined by s. Finally, $s \in \hat{X}_R$, for if $p(s) = 0$, then $\phi(p) = 0$, so $p \notin R(X)^{-1}$, so p must vanish on X. Thus $\text{Spec } R(X) = \hat{X}_R$.

Suppose $\hat{X} = \hat{X}_R$. Then any polynomial q which has no zeroes on X has no zeroes on $\hat{X}$ either, so $q^{-1} \in P(X)$. Thus $P(X) = R(X)$ if and only if $\hat{X} = \hat{X}_R$.

Let us examine the maximal ideal space of the big disk algebra A, introduced on Page 6. Let $\phi \in \text{Spec } A$, and put $s_i = \phi(z_i)$ for $i = 1,2$. Then $|s_i| \leq 1$, $i = 1,2$, and since for all n,m with $n + m\alpha \geq 0$ we have $|\phi(z_1^n z_2^m)| = |s_1^n s_2^m| \leq 1$, it follows that $n\log|s_1| + m\log|s_2| \leq 0$ whenever $n + m\alpha \geq 0$, so $\log|s_2| = \alpha\log|s_1|$, i.e., $|s_2| = |s_1|^\alpha$. Since ϕ is clearly determined by (s_1,s_2), we have a one-one continuous map of $\text{Spec } A$ into $\{(s_1,s_2) \in \mathbb{C}^2 : |s_1| \leq 1, |s_2| = |s_1|^\alpha\} = K$. Let now (s_1,s_2) be any point of K, other than $(0,0)$. Then $s_2 = e^{it}s_1^\alpha$ for some real t, some determination of s_1^α, i.e., there exists ζ, $\text{Re}\zeta \leq 0$, with $s_1 = e^\zeta$, $s_2 = e^{it}e^{\alpha\zeta}$. Let f be any "trigonometric polynomial" in A, i.e., a finite sum of the form $\sum c_{nm} z_1^n z_2^m$. Put

$F(s) = \sum c_{nm} e^{(n+m\alpha)s} e^{imt}$, for $s \in \mathbb{C}$, $\mathrm{Re}\, s \leq 0$. Then F is holomorphic in $\{\mathrm{Re}\, s < 0\}$, continuous and bounded in $\{\mathrm{Re}\, s \leq 0\}$. By the maximum modulus principle, (or more precisely, by a Phragmén-Lindelöf theorem) it follows that $|F(\zeta)| \leq \sup\{|F(i\eta)| : \eta \text{ real}\}$. But for η real, $F(i\eta) = \sum c_{nm} e^{in\eta} e^{im(\alpha\eta+t)}$, a value of f on $\Gamma \times \Gamma$. Thus $|F(\zeta)| \leq \|f\|$; but the map $f \to F(\zeta)$ is evidently a multiplicative linear functional on the algebra of such trigonometric polynomials, and hence the extension to A is a multiplicative linear functional on A. Hence the image of Spec A under the map $\phi \to (\phi(z_1),\phi(z_2))$ contains $K\backslash\{(0,0)\}$, and hence $= K$. We observe that Spec A decomposes into the following parts: $\Gamma \times \Gamma$, the original space on which A was defined; $(0,0)$, the "origin" of the big disk; a union (uncountable) of continuous images of the left half-plane, on each of which the functions in A (or more precisely, their Gelfand transforms) are holomorphic. We observe that each half plane is dense in Spec A.

1-4 THE FUNCTIONAL CALCULUS

If A is a function algebra on X, and $f \in A$, it is immediate from the definitions that $F \circ f \in A$ if either $F \in P(f(X))$ or $F \in R(\text{spec } f)$. One of the notable features of the Gelfand theory is a version of this for general Banach algebras.

Let A be a Banach algebra with unit, $f \in A$, and suppose F is holomorphic in some neighborhood U of spec f. Choose a contour γ in U enclosing spec f (this means that γ is a finite union of rectifiable closed curves lying in U, and the winding number of γ with respect to any point of spec f is 1). We define $F(f) = \frac{1}{2\pi i}\int_\gamma F(\zeta)(\zeta - f)^{-1}d\zeta$, where the vector-valued integral is defined, as to be expected, as the limit of Riemann-Stieltjes sums $\sum_1^n F(\zeta_j)(\zeta_j - f)^{-1}(\zeta_j - \zeta_{j-1})$. The same argument that shows that the Riemann-Stieltjes integral of a continuous scalar function exists shows that $F(f)$ is well-defined (the vector-valued integrand is continuous by Corollary 1.2.2). For any $\phi \in A^*$, passing through the approximating sums, we find

$\phi(F(f)) = \frac{1}{2\pi i}\int_\gamma F(\zeta)\phi[(\zeta - f)^{-1}]d\zeta$; as we have seen, $\phi[(\zeta - f)^{-1}]$ is a holomorphic function of ζ outside spec f; it follows from Cauchy's theorem that $\phi(F(f))$ is independent of the choice of γ. Since $\phi \in A^*$ was arbitrary, it follows that F(f) does not depend on the choice of γ. If $\phi \in$ Spec A, $\phi[(\zeta - f)^{-1}] = [\zeta - \phi(f)]^{-1}$, and from the Cauchy integral formula we find that $\phi(F(f)) = F(\phi(f))$. Thus $\widehat{F(f)} = F(\hat{f})$, and in particular, spec F(f) = F(spec f). It can be shown that $FG(f) = F(f)G(f)$, whenever F and G are holomorphic in a neighborhood of spec f.

Let us consider the following special case. Let X be a compact plane set, with bounded complementary components $G_1, G_2, \ldots$. Choose $a_n \in G_n$ for each n, and let A be the uniform closure on X of the algebra of all rational functions whose only (finite) poles are among the $\{a_n\}$. The arguments used in the last section in determining Spec P(X) show that spec z = X. The discussion above now shows that A contains every function holomorphic in a neighborhood of X. In particular, if X has connected complement, every function holomorphic in a neighborhood can be approximated uniformly on X by polynomials. This is a classical result known as Runge's theorem, and the proof we have just given is indeed (stripped of the fancy language) the classical proof.

In spec f is contained in a disk D, and F is holomorphic in D, we can also define $F(f)$ by a Taylor series. For if $D = \{s \in \mathbb{C} : |s - c| < R\}$, then for $s \in D$ we have $F(s) = \sum_0^\infty a_n(s - c)^n$, where $\lim\sup|a_n|^{1/n} \leq 1/R$. Now spec $f \subset D$ implies $\text{spec}(f - c) \subset \{s : |s| < R\}$, whence $\lim\|(f - c)^n\|^{1/n} < r < R$. It follows that $\sum a_n(f - c)^n$ is majorized by the geometric series $\sum(\frac{r}{R})^n$, hence converges to an element of A which we denote by $F(f)$. It is easy to see that this definition agrees with the one given by Cauchy's integral formula. Power series in a Banach algebra element may be manipulated with the same ease as scalar power series; the crucial fact being that absolute convergence $(\sum|a_n|\|(f - c)^n\| < \infty)$ implies unconditional convergence. We illustrate with the most important special case.

DEFINITION. Let A be a Banach algebra with unit. For each $f \in A$, we define $\exp f = \sum_0^\infty \frac{f^n}{n!}$.

LEMMA 1.4.1. *If* f *and* g *commute, then* $\exp(f + g) = \exp f \cdot \exp g$.

Proof. $\exp(f + g) = \sum_0^\infty \frac{(f + g)^n}{n!}$

$$= \sum_{n=0}^\infty \frac{1}{n!} \sum_{j+k=n} \frac{n!}{j!k!} f^j g^k$$

$$= \left(\sum_{j=0}^\infty \frac{f^j}{j!}\right)\left(\sum_{k=0}^\infty \frac{g^k}{k!}\right) = \exp f \cdot \exp g,$$

the binomial theorem being purely algebraic, and the rearranging of sums being justified by absolute convergence.

LEMMA 1.4.2. *If* $f \in A$ *and* $\|1 - f\| < 1$, *there exists* $g \in A$ *such that* $\exp g = f$.

Proof. Put $g = -\sum_1^\infty \frac{(1 - f)^n}{n}$; the series is majorized by the convergent series $\sum \|1 - f\|^n$, so g is well defined. To see that $\exp g = f$, we may argue as follows: for each $k \geq 1$, $g^k = \sum_1^\infty a_{nk}(1 - f)^n$, where the complex coefficients a_{nk} are determined by the Cauchy rule for multiplying power series, hence do not depend on f. Then

$$\exp g = \sum_0^\infty \frac{g^k}{k!} = 1 + \sum_{n=1}^\infty \Big(\sum_{k=1}^\infty \frac{a_{nk}}{k!}\Big)(1 - f)^n,$$

the interchange in order of summation being justified by absolute convergence. Now it is well known that $\exp g = f$ when $f \in \mathbb{C}$, and hence the coefficient of $(1 - f)^n$ above is 0 when $n > 1$, -1 when $n = 1$. Thus $\exp g = f$, and the lemma is proved.

When A is a Banach algebra with unit, we define $\exp A = \{\exp f : f \in A\}$. From Lemma 1.4.1, we have $\exp f \cdot \exp(-f) = \exp 0 = 1$ for any $f \in A$, so $\exp A \subset A^{-1}$.

THEOREM 1.4.3. *Let* A *be a commutative Banach algebra with unit. Then* $\exp A$ *is precisely the connected component of* 1 *in* A^{-1}.

Proof. We observe first that for any $g \in A$, the map $t \to \exp tg (0 \leq t \leq 1)$ is a path in $\exp A$ connecting 1 to $\exp g$, so $\exp A$ is connected. Now if $f = \exp h$, and $\| f - g \| < \| f^{-1} \|^{-1}$, then

$\|1 - f^{-1}g\| < 1$, so by Lemma 1.4.2 we have $f^{-1}g = \exp k$ for some $k \in A$, and hence $g = \exp h \exp k = \exp(h + k) \in \exp A$. Thus $\exp A$ is open. Finally, if $f \in A^{-1}$ and f is in the closure of $\exp A$, there exists $g \in \exp A$ with $\|g - f\| < \|f^{-1}\|^{-1}$, so $\|gf^{-1} - 1\| < 1$, so $gf^{-1} \in \exp A$, and so $f \in \exp A$. Thus $\exp A$ is connected, open and closed in A^{-1}, and $1 \in \exp A$, so the theorem is proved.

Since $\exp A \subset A^{-1}$, it is clear that $\phi(\exp f) \neq 0$ for every $\phi \in \text{Spec } A$. It is a remarkable fact that this property singles out the multiplicative linear functionals on a commutative Banach algebra with unit. The theorem is due to Gleason [3], and the proof uses an elementary result of complex function theory which is sometimes omitted from introductory courses.

LEMMA. *Let* G *be an entire function, and suppose there exist constants* K, N *such that* $\text{Re}G(s) \leq K|s|^N$ *for every* $s \in \mathbb{C}$, $|s|$ *sufficiently large. Then* G *is a polynomial of degree* $\leq N$.

Proof. We can assume $G(0) = 0$. Let $G = \sum_1^\infty a_n z^n$. Then $\text{Re}G(re^{i\theta}) = \sum_1^\infty r^n(\text{Re}a_n\cos n\theta - \text{Im}a_n\sin n\theta)$. Then $\frac{1}{\pi}\int_0^{2\pi} \text{Re}G(re^{i\theta})\cos k\theta d\theta = r^k\text{Re}a_k$, and $\frac{1}{\pi}\int_0^{2\pi} \text{Re}G(re^{i\theta})\sin k\theta d\theta = r^k\text{Im}a_k$, for $k = 1,2,\ldots$, while $\int_0^{2\pi} \text{Re}G(re^{i\theta})d\theta = 0$. It follows that

$$\pm \text{Re}\, a_k = \frac{1}{\pi r^k}\int_0^{2\pi} \text{Re}\, G(re^{i\theta})(1\pm\cos k\theta)d\theta \leq \frac{2K}{r^{N-k}}$$

and $\pm \text{Im}\, a_k = \frac{1}{\pi r^k}\int_0^{2\pi} \text{Re}\, G(re^{i\theta})(1\pm\sin k\theta)d\theta \leq \frac{2K}{r^{N-k}}$, since $\text{Re}G(re^{i\theta}) \leq Kr^N$ and $0 \leq 1 \pm \cos k\theta \leq 2$, $0 \leq 1 \pm \sin k\theta \leq 2$. Letting $r \to \infty$, we find that $|\text{Re}a_k| = |\text{Im}a_k| = 0$ for $k > N$, which was to be proved.

We refer to this lemma as the "real part Liouville theorem".

THEOREM 1.4.4. *Let* A *be a commutative Banach algebra with unit, and let* ϕ *be a linear functional on* A *with the property that* $\phi(\exp f) \neq 0$ *for all* $f \in A$, $\phi(1) = 1$. *Then* $\phi \in \text{Spec } A$.

Proof. We first observe that ϕ is a continuous linear functional, in fact that $\|\phi\| = 1$. For if

$f \in A$ and $\|f\| < 1$, for every $s \in \mathbb{C}$, $|s| \geq 1$, we have by Lemma 1.4.2 that $1 - \frac{f}{s} \in \exp A$, and hence $s - \phi(f) \neq 0$. Thus $|\phi(f)| < 1$ whenever $\|f\| < 1$, i.e., $\|\phi\| = 1$. In view of the identity $fg = \frac{1}{4}[(f + g)^2 - (f - g)^2]$, in order to show that ϕ is multiplicative it suffices to show that $\phi(f^2) = [\phi(f)]^2$ for all $f \in A$. Let $f \in A$; for each $s \in \mathbb{C}$, put $F(s) = \phi(\exp sf)$. Thus

$$F(s) = \phi(\sum_0^\infty \frac{s^n f^n}{n!}) = \sum_0^\infty \frac{\phi(f^n)}{n!} s^n,$$

so F is an entire function without zeroes, and $|F(s)| \leq \sum \frac{\|f\|^n}{n!} |s|^n = \exp|s|\|f\|$. Thus $F = \exp G$, where G is entire and $\operatorname{Re} G(s) \leq \|f\||s|$ for all $s \in \mathbb{C}$. Since $F(0) = 1$, we can assume $G(0) = 0$. By the "real part Liouville theorem" above, it follows that $G = az$ for some constant a, so $F = e^{az} = \sum_0^\infty \frac{a^n}{n!} z^n$. Equating coefficients, we thus have $\phi(f^n) = a^n = [\phi(f)]^n$ for all n, and in particular for $n = 2$, which proves the theorem.

An obvious corollary is that a linear functional ϕ on A, with $\phi(1) = 1$, is a multiplicative linear functional if and only if $\phi(f) \neq 0$ for all $f \in A^{-1}$.

If we assume to start with that ϕ is continuous, we can apply Gleason's argument with an otherwise weaker hypothesis.

THEOREM 1.4.5. *Let* $\mathcal{F}$ *be a set of generators for* A, *a commutative Banach algebra with unit. Let* $\phi \in A^*$, $\phi(1) = 1$ *and suppose that* $\phi(\exp f) \neq 0$ *for every* f *in the linear span of* $\mathcal{F}$. *Then* $\phi \in \text{Spec } A$.

Proof. Let g be any element in the linear span of $\mathcal{F}$, so $g = \sum_1^n s_j f_j$, where $s_j \in \mathbb{C}$, $f_j \in \mathcal{F}$. Define F by $F(\zeta) = \phi(\exp \zeta g) = \sum_0^\infty \frac{\phi(g^k)}{k!} \zeta^k$. As before, F is an entire function with no zeroes, $F(0) = 1$ and $|F(\zeta)| \leq \|\phi\| \exp(\|f\| |\zeta|)$, so applying the real part Liouville theorem we have $F = \exp az$ for some a, and thus $\phi(g^k) = [\phi(g)]^k$ for every k. Now

$$\phi(g^k) = \sum_j C_j^k \phi(f^j) s^j \tag{1}$$

and

$$[\phi(g)]^k = \sum_j C_j^k [\phi(f)]^j s^j, \tag{2}$$

where the sums are taken over all $j = (j_1, \dots, j_n)$ with $j_1 + \cdots\cdots + j_n = k$, c_j^k denotes the multinomial coefficient $\frac{k!}{j_1! \cdots\cdots j_n!}$, and we use the abbreviations

$$f^j = f_1^{j_1} \cdots\cdots f_n^{j_n}, \quad s^j = s_1^{j_1} \cdots\cdots s_n^{j_n}$$

$$[\phi(f)]^j = \phi(f_1)^{j_1} \cdots\cdots \phi(f_n)^{j_n}.$$

Since the polynomials (1) and (2) in $s_1, \dots, s_n$ are equal for all values of $s_1, \dots, s_n$, their coefficients are equal, i.e.,

$$\phi(f_1^{j_1} \cdots\cdots f_n^{j_n}) = \phi(f_1)^{j_1} \cdots\cdots \phi(f_n)^{j_n}.$$

It follows immediately that $\phi(pq) = \phi(p)\phi(q)$ for all polynomials p and q in the generators, and hence (again taking account of the continuity of ϕ) that ϕ is a multiplicative linear functional. The theorem is proved.

If X is a compact subset of $\mathbb{C}^n$, and ϕ a continuous linear functional on $C(X)$, the entire function Φ of n variables defined by $\Phi(s_1, \dots, s_n) = \phi(\exp \sum_1^n s_j z_j)$ is known as the *Laplace transform* of ϕ. Thus Gleason's theorem tells us: if $\phi \in C(X)^*$ and $\phi(1) = 1$, then (the restriction of) ϕ is a multiplicative linear functional on $P(X)$ if and only if the Laplace transform of ϕ never vanishes. It seems that there should be applications of this result, but we know of none.

1-5 ANALYTIC STRUCTURE

In the handful of examples that we have looked at, when A was a function algebra on X and Spec A was strictly larger than X, the reason was that the functions in A were analytic on Spec $A \setminus X$ (or, as in the big disk algebra, on substantial parts of Spec $A \setminus X$). At one time, it was conjectured that whenever Spec A is larger than X, there must be "analytic structure" somewhere in Spec A. As to what "analytic structure" should mean, it would seem that a minimum requirement might be: there is an imbedding Φ of a disk in Spec A, such that the functions $\hat{f} \circ \Phi$ are analytic, for every $f \in A$. Besides the known examples, support for this conjecture came from the work of Wermer in two different contexts. One of Wermer's theorems was this: *let* J *be an analytic closed curve in* $\mathbb{C}^n$. *Then either* J *is polynomially convex* (i.e., J = Spec P(J), *in which case* P(J) = C(J), *or else* $\hat{J}$ = Spec P(J) *is a finite bordered Riemann surface, with perhaps a finite number of points identified.* (This theorem has been improved, to weaken the requirement of analyticity to continuous differentiability: the major step due to Bishop, and important contributions due to Royden and Stolzenberg. See Stolzenberg [4] for the best current version, and for the references.)

The other theorem of Wermer's to which we referred is this: *if* ReA, *the real parts of the functions in* A, *is dense in* $C_R(X)$, *then for each* $\phi \in$ Spec A, *one of the following alternatives holds:*

i) $\|\phi - \psi\| = 2$ *for every* $\psi \in$ Spec A, $\psi \neq \phi$;

ii) *there exists a continuous one-one map* Φ *of the open unit disk onto* $P = \{\psi \in \text{Spec } A : \|\phi - \psi\| < 2\}$, *bicontinuous if* P *is given the metric topology, such that* $\hat{f} \circ \Phi$ *is holomorphic for each* $f \in A$. We shall prove this theorem in Chapter IV.

However, the hope that analytic structure is always present when Spec A $\neq$ X was shattered by an example devised by Stolzenberg [1]; he found a set X in $\mathbb{C}^3$, with $\hat{X}$ properly containing X, such that X contains no "analytic disks", in the sense described above.

If one cannot expect to have analytic disks in Spec A, one can still ask if there are more primitive aspects of analyticity left. In Chapter II, we discuss the presence in function algebras of such phenomena as anti-symmetry (real valued holomorphic functions are constant on connected sets), Schwarz's lemma, and the Jensen inequality. In the next section, we discuss a more direct aspect of holomorphic functions, viz., their differentiability. In this section, we present a theorem of Gleason which deduces the presence of analytic structure from algebraic properties.

We shall need the notion of analytic variety.

DEFINITION. Let G be an open subset of $\mathbb{C}^n$. A subset V of G is called an *analytic variety* in G if for each point $s \in G$ there exists an open neighborhood U of s, and a finite set

$\{f_1, \ldots, f_r\}$ of functions holomorphic in U, such that $V \cap U = \{\zeta \in U : f_j(\zeta) = 0 \text{ for } 1 \leq j \leq r\}$.

The finiteness of the defining family of functions is not essential. Thus, to show that a subset V of the open set G is an analytic variety in G, it suffices to show that for every $s \in G\backslash V$ there exists f holomorphic in G, vanishing on V, with $f(s) = 1$. (This is a simple consequence of the fact that the ring of convergent power series in n variables is Noetherian; for the proof, we refer the reader to the book of Gunning and Rossi [1].)

It is not necessary to know any of the deep theory of analytic varieties to understand Gleason's theorem, but to help appreciate its import in our context, we state the following fact: let V be an analytic variety in G. Then for each non-isolated point $s \in V$, there exists a one-one continuous map Φ of the open unit disk Δ into V, with $\Phi(0) = s$, such that $f \circ \Phi$ is holomorphic in Δ whenever f is holomorphic in G. Again, we refer to Gunning and Rossi for the proof.

THEOREM 1.5.1 (Gleason [2]). *Let* A *be a commutative Banach algebra with unit,* $\phi \in \text{Spec } A$. *Suppose that the maximal ideal* $M = \ker \phi$ *is finitely generated in the algebraic sense,* i.e., *there exist* $f_1, \dots, f_n \in M$ *such that*

$$M = \{\sum f_j g_j : g_j \in A, 1 \leq j \leq n\}.$$

Then there exists $\varepsilon > 0$, *and an analytic variety* V *in the polydisk* $\Delta(0,\varepsilon) = \{s \in \mathbb{C}^n : |s_j| < \varepsilon, 1 \leq j \leq n\}$, *with the following property: let* U *be the neighborhood of* ϕ *in* Spec A *defined by* $U = \{\psi \in \text{Spec } A : |\hat{f}_j(\psi)| < \varepsilon, 1 \leq j \leq n\}$, *and let* $F : U \to \Delta(0,\varepsilon)$ *be defined by* $F(\psi) = (\hat{f}_1(\psi), \dots, \hat{f}_n(\psi))$. *Then* F *is a homeomorphism of* U *onto* V, *and for each* $g \in A$, *there exists* $\tilde{g}$ *holomorphic in* $\Delta(0,\varepsilon)$ *such that* $\hat{g}(\psi) = \tilde{g}(F(\psi))$ *for all* $\psi \in U$.

Proof. Consider the Banach space $A^n = A \times \cdots \times A$, with the norm $\|(g_1, \dots, g_n)\| = \max\{\|g_j\|\}$. Define $T : A^n \to M$ by $T(g_1, \dots, g_n) = \sum f_i g_i$. Evidently, T is a continuous linear map, and by hypothesis T is onto. Hence, by the open mapping theorem, there exists $K > 0$ such that for every

$g \in M$ there exist $g_1, \ldots, g_n \in A$ such that $g = \sum f_j g_j$ and $\|g_j\| \leq \frac{1}{2} K\|g\|$ for $j = 1, \ldots, n$. It follows that for every $g \in A$, there exist $g_j \in A$ $(j = 1, \ldots, n)$ such that $\|g_j\| \leq K\|g\|$ and

$$g = \phi(g) + \sum f_j g_j .$$

Similarly, for each j we find $g_{jk} \in A$ with $g_j = \phi(g_j) + \sum_{k=1}^{n} f_k g_{jk}$, and $\|g_{jk}\| \leq K\|g_j\| \leq K^2\|g\|$ for $k = 1, \ldots, n$. Thus

$$g = \phi(g) + \sum_{j=1}^{n} \phi(g_j) f_j + \sum_{j,k=1}^{n} f_j f_k g_{jk},$$

where $\|g_{jk}\| \leq K^2\|g\|$ for $j,k = 1, \ldots, n$. By induction, we find for every positive integer r, a polynomial P_r in n variables, with complex coefficients, of degree $\leq r - 1$, such that

$$g = P_r(f_1, \ldots, f_n) + \sum_{j_1, \ldots, j_r = 1}^{n} g_{j_1 \ldots j_r} f_{j_1} \cdot \ldots \cdot f_{j_r}$$

with $g_{j_1 \ldots j_r} \in A$, and $\|g_{j_1 \ldots j_r}\| \leq K^r \|g\|$ for every multi-index $j_1 \cdot \ldots \cdot j_r$. Choose $\varepsilon > 0$ so that $\eta = \varepsilon n K < 1$. Let $U = \{\psi \in \text{Spec } A :$ $|\psi(f_j)| < \varepsilon$ for $j = 1, \ldots, n\}$, so U is an open neighborhood of ϕ. We note that $\overline{U}$, the closure of U, is contained in $\{\psi : |\psi(f_j)| \leq \varepsilon, 1 \leq j \leq n\}$. Then for $\psi \in \overline{U}$,

$$\begin{aligned} &|\hat{g}(\psi) - P_r(\hat{f}_1, \ldots, \hat{f}_n)(\psi)| \\ &\leq \sum_{j_1,\ldots,j_r=1}^{n} K^r \|g\| \varepsilon^r \\ &= (\varepsilon n K)^r \|g\| = \eta^r \|g\|. \end{aligned}$$

Thus $P_r(\hat{f}_1, \ldots, \hat{f}_n)$ converges uniformly to $\hat{g}$ on $\overline{U}$. Since $\hat{A}$ separates the points of Spec A, it follows that $f_1, \ldots, f_n$ separate the points of $\overline{U}$. Hence the map F defined in the statement of the theorem is a homeomorphism of $\overline{U}$ onto its image, and hence of U onto its image V. We observe that for each r,

$$P_{r+1} - P_r = \sum_{j_1,\ldots,j_r=1}^{n} C_{j_1 \ldots j_r} z_{j_1} \cdot \ldots \cdot z_{j_r}$$

where $z_1, \ldots, z_n$ are the coordinates of $\mathbb{C}^n$ (or indeterminates), and $C_{j_1 \ldots j_r} = \phi(g_{j_1 \ldots j_r})$, so $|C_{j_1 \ldots j_r}| \leq K^r \|g\|$. Thus, the polynomial (functions) $P_r(z_1, \ldots, z_n)$ converge uniformly on the closed polydisk $\overline{\Delta}(0,\varepsilon)$, and hence their limit is a function $\tilde{g}$ holomorphic in $\Delta(0,\varepsilon)$.

Evidently, $\hat{g}(\psi) = \tilde{g}(F(\psi))$ for each $\psi \in U$. It remains to show that V is an analytic variety, i.e., to show that for any $s \in \Delta(0,\varepsilon)\backslash V$, there exists h holomorphic in $\Delta(0,\varepsilon)$ with $h(s) = 1$ and $h(t) = 0$ for every $t \in V$. Now if $s = (s_1, \ldots, s_n) \in \Delta(0,\varepsilon)\backslash V$, then $\hat{f}_1 - s_1, \ldots, \hat{f}_n - s_n$ have no common zero in U (by definition of V), nor in Spec $A\backslash U$ (by definition of U). Hence (Corollary 1.2.13) there exist $g_1, \ldots, g_n \in A$ such that $\sum(f_j - s_j)g_j = 1$. Put $h = 1 - \sum(z_j - s_j)\tilde{g}_j$. It is clear that h fulfills the requirements. The proof is finished.

1-6 POINT DERIVATIONS

DEFINITION. Let A be a commutative Banach algebra with unit, and let $\phi \in$ Spec A. We say that ψ is a *point derivation* on A at ϕ if ψ is a linear functional on A, and if

$$\psi(fg) = \psi(f)\phi(g) + \phi(f)\psi(g)$$

whenever $f,g \in A$ (Leibniz' rule). A *bounded point derivation* is a point derivation which is bounded (continuous) as a linear functional.

If ψ is a point derivation at ϕ, it is clear that $\psi(1) = 0$, and that $\psi(fg) = 0$ whenever $\phi(f) = \phi(g) = 0$. Conversely, if ψ is a linear functional with these properties, it is easily seen that ψ is a point derivation at ϕ: for

$$\psi[(f - \phi(f))(g - \phi(g))] = 0 \text{ for any } f,g \in A,$$

and multiplying out and using linearity, we obtain Leibniz' rule. We can formulate this remark in terms of ideals. Let M be the maximal ideal associated with ϕ, i.e., $M = \ker \phi$, and let M^2 denote the linear span of $\{fg : f,g \in M\}$. Then M^2 is an ideal in A, though not necessarily closed, and $\mathbb{C} + M^2$ is a subalgebra of A. A point derivation at ϕ is a linear functional on A which annihilates $\mathbb{C} + M^2$; it follows that there exists a non-zero point derivation at ϕ if and only if $M^2 \neq M$, and there exists a bounded point derivation at ϕ if and only if M^2 is not dense in M.

If $A = C(X)$, there exists no non-zero point derivation on A. For if x is any point of X, and $f \in A$, $f(x) = 0$, we can write $f = gh$, where $g(x) = h(x) = 0$, $g,h \in A$: for instance, $g = \sqrt{|f|}$, $h = g\,sgn f$.

If A is the disk algebra, there is an obvious point derivation D_s at each point s of the open disk, given by $D_s f = f'(s)$. If $f \in A$, we can write $f = f(s) + (z - s)g$ for some $g \in A$; so if D any derivation at s, $Df = D[(z - s)g]$ $= D(z - s)g(s) = (Dz)\cdot g(s) = (Dz)f'(s) = (Dz)D_s f$. Thus every derivation at s is a multiple of D_s. If $|s| = 1$, and D a derivation at s, then $Dz = D(z - s) = 0$, since $\sqrt{z - s} \in A$, so $Df = 0$ whenever f a polynomial in z. This does not immediately exclude the possibility of a non-zero (unbounded) point derivation at s. By using deeper results of function theory (the Nevanlinna "inner-outer" factorization) one can show that for any $f \in A$, $f(s) = 0$, there exist $g,h \in A$, $g(s) = h(s) = 0$, such that $f = gh$; thus, there is no non-zero point derivation at s. We shall see this as a result of Banach algebra methods later in this section.

Point derivations may occur even in the absence of any analytic structure. It was only very recently shown, by Brian Cole, that there exist function algebras, other than $C(X)$, which admit no non-zero point derivation. One of Cole's examples is given in the appendix.

The next theorem has been known by various people for many years, but apparently never published.

THEOREM 1.6.1. *Let* A *be a commutative Banach algebra with unit, and* ϕ *a linear functional on* A *(not necessarily continuous). Suppose that* $\ker \phi$ *is a subalgebra of* A. *Then*

i) *if* $\phi(1) \neq 0$, *then* ϕ *is a scalar multiple of a multiplicative linear functional;*

ii) *if* $\phi(1) = 0$, *then either there exist* $\theta, \psi \in \operatorname{Spec} A$ *such that* ϕ *is a scalar multiple of* $\theta - \psi$, *or there exists* $\theta \in \operatorname{Spec} A$ *such that* ϕ *is a point derivation at* θ.

Proof. If $\phi(1) \neq 0$, we may assume $\phi(1) = 1$. Then, for every $f, g \in A$, we have

$$\phi(fg) = \phi([f - \phi(f)][g - \phi(g)]) + \phi(f)\phi(g).$$

Since $\phi(f - \phi(f)) = 0 = \phi(g - \phi(g))$, and $\ker \phi$

is an algebra, it follows that $\phi(fg) = \phi(f)\phi(g)$, and i) is proved.

Now suppose $\phi(1) = 0$. If there exist $\theta, \psi \in \text{Spec } A$, $\theta \neq \psi$, such that $\theta(f) = \psi(f)$ for every $f \in \ker \phi$, then $\ker \phi \subset \ker(\theta - \psi)$, so ϕ is a scalar multiple of $\theta - \psi$. We are left with the case: $\phi(1) = 0$, *and for every* $\theta, \psi \in \text{Spec } A$ $(\theta \neq \psi)$ *there exists* $f \in \ker \phi$ *with* $\theta(f) \neq \psi(f)$. We may assume $\phi \neq 0$. Choose $e_0 \in A$ such that $\phi(e_0) = 1$, and put $e = e_0 - \frac{1}{2}\phi(e_0^2)$. Then $\phi(e) = 1$, and $\phi(e^2) = 0$. Define the linear functional θ on A by $\theta(f) = \phi(ef)$. Since $f - \phi(f)e \in \ker \phi$ for every $f \in A$, and $\ker \phi$ is an algebra, we have for every $f, g \in A$:

$$\begin{aligned} 0 &= \phi([f - \phi(f)e][g - \phi(g)e]) \\ &= \phi(fg) - \phi(f)\phi(eg) - \phi(g)\phi(ef) \\ &\quad + \phi(f)\phi(g)\phi(e^2), \end{aligned}$$

so

$$\phi(fg) = \phi(f)\theta(g) + \phi(g)\theta(f). \qquad (*)$$

Let $J = (\ker \phi) \cap (\ker \theta)$. We see at once from (*) that J is an ideal in A, proper since $\theta(1) = 1$. We note that for every $f \in A$,

$$f - \theta(f) - \phi(f)e \in J, \qquad (**)$$

as we see from $\phi(1) = \theta(e) = 0$, $\phi(e) = \theta(1) = 1$. Now J is contained in a maximal ideal of A (Lemma 1.2.10), and thus there exists $\psi \in \text{Spec } A$ such that $J \subset \ker \psi$ (Theorem 1.2.12). From (**) we have $\psi(f) = \theta(f)$ for every $f \in \ker \phi$, and from our assumption on ϕ it follows that ψ is uniquely determined. We wish to show that $\psi = \theta$. Using (**), we see this is equivalent to showing that $\psi(e) = 0$. Now if $\psi(e) \neq 0$, then $e + \psi(e) \notin \ker \psi$; since $\ker \psi$ is the unique maximal ideal containing J, it follows that $e + \psi(e)$ and J generate the unit ideal, i.e., that there exists $g \in A$ such that $(e + \psi(e))g + 1 \in J$. But then, multiplying by $e - \psi(e)$, we have $(e^2 - \psi(e^2))g + e - \psi(e) \in J$. Now $\psi(e^2) = \theta(e^2)$ since $e^2 \in \ker \phi$, so $e^2 - \psi(e^2) \in J$, and hence $e - \psi(e) \in J$. But this is impossible: $\phi(e) = 1$, $\phi(1) = 0$. This contradiction shows that $\psi(e) = 0$. Thus $\theta = \psi \in \text{Spec } A$, and (*) shows that ϕ is a point derivation at θ, concluding the proof.

A similar theorem, concerning subalgebras of finite codimension in A, was found by Gamelin [1].

A simple-minded approach to the problem of constructing point derivations might run as follows. Suppose $\phi \in \text{Spec } A$ is not isolated in the metric topology, so there exist $\phi_n \in \text{Spec } A$, $n = 1,2, \ldots$, with $\|\phi - \phi_n\| \to 0$. Put $\psi_n = \frac{\phi - \phi_n}{\|\phi - \phi_n\|}$; then $\psi_n \in A^*$, and $\|\psi_n\| = 1$. Let ψ be any cluster point of $\{\psi_n\}$, in the weak-* topology of A^*. It is clear that $\psi(1) = 0$, and $\|\psi\| \leq 1$. If $\phi(f) = \phi(g) = 0$, then $|\psi_n(fg)| \leq |\phi_n(f)| \|g\| \to 0$ since $\phi_n \to \phi$, hence $\psi(fg) = 0$. Thus ψ is a bounded point derivation at ϕ. The trouble with this argument is that ψ might be the zero derivation, which we can obtain with less trouble. In fact, there need not exist bounded point derivations (other than zero) even at non-isolated (metrically) points of Spec A. However, we do have a theorem for the existence of (possibly unbounded) non-zero point derivations. This theorem is due to the author [2].

THEOREM 1.6.2. *Let* A *be a commutative Banach algebra with unit, let* $\phi \in \text{Spec } A$. *Suppose there exists no non-zero point derivation at* ϕ. *Then* ϕ *is an isolated point of* Spec A, *in the metric topology.*

Proof. As above, let $M = \ker \phi$ and M^2 the linear span of $\{fg : f,g \in M\}$. The hypothesis is then that $M^2 = M$. Let

$$U = \{fg : \|f\| \leq 1, \|g\| \leq 1, f,g \in M\},$$

and let K be the convex hull of U,

$$K = \{ \sum_{j \in I} t_j f_j : I \text{ finite}, t_j \geq 0, \sum t_j = 1, f_i \in U\}.$$

Then $M^2 = \bigcup_1^\infty nK$ (where $nK = \{nf : f \in K\}$). Since $M^2 = M$, and M is a Banach space, it follows from the Baire category theorem that for some n, nK is somewhere dense, i.e., the closure of nK has non-empty interior. Since K is convex and symmetric, it follows that the closure of nK contains a neighborhood of the origin in M. Thus, there exists $\delta > 0$ such that K is dense in

$\{f \in M : \|f\| \leq \delta\}$. Hence for any $\theta \in M^*$,

$$\begin{aligned}\delta\|\theta\| &= \sup\{\delta|\theta(f)| : f \in M, \|f\| \leq 1\} \\ &= \sup\{|\theta(f)| : f \in M, \|f\| \leq \delta\} \\ &\leq \sup\{|\theta(f)| : f \in K\}.\end{aligned}$$

Now suppose $\psi \in \text{Spec } A$. Let θ denote the restriction of ψ to M. Then $\|\theta\| \leq \|\phi - \psi\|$. If $f \in K$, then there exist $f_j, g_j \in M$, $(1 \leq j \leq n)$ with $\|f_j\| \leq 1$, $\|g_j\| \leq 1$ and $t_j \geq 0$, $\sum t_j = 1$, such that $f = \sum t_j f_j g_j$. Then

$$\theta(f) = \sum t_j \theta(f_j g_j) = \sum t_j \theta(f_j)\theta(g_j)$$

so $|\theta(f)| \leq \sum t_j \|\theta\|^2 \|f_j\| \|g_j\| \leq \|\theta\|^2$. Thus $\delta\|\theta\| \leq \|\theta\|^2$, so $\|\theta\| \geq \delta$ unless $\theta = 0$, therefore $\|\phi - \psi\| \geq \delta$ for $\psi \in \text{Spec } A$, $\psi \neq \phi$. The theorem is proved.

The sophisticated reader will observe that the proof consisted of applying the open mapping theorem to the natural map of the tensor product $M \otimes M$ into M.

The converse of Theorem 1.6.2 does not hold. In fact, Sidney [2] has constructed an example where $\|\phi - \psi\| = 2$ for all $\psi \in \text{Spec } A, \psi \neq \phi$, yet

ϕ admits a bounded point derivation. The reader is referred to this paper (and Sidney [1]) for more about point derivations.

We do have, however, a condition which ensures the non-existence of point derivations, due to Paul Cohen.

DEFINITION. Let A be a commutative Banach algebra with unit, M a maximal ideal of A. We say that M has an *approximate identity* if there exists a constant K such that for every $\varepsilon > 0$, every $f_1, \ldots, f_n \in M$, there exists $e \in M$, $\|e\| \leq K$, such that $\|ef_j - f_j\| < \varepsilon$ for $j = 1, \ldots, n$. (In other words, there exists a *bounded net* $\{e_\alpha\}$ in M such that $e_\alpha f \to f$ for every $f \in M$.)

The notion of approximate identity is a familiar one in harmonic analysis. Let us see what it amounts to for function algebras.

LEMMA 1.6.3. *Let* A *be a function algebra on* X, *and* $x \in X$. *The the following are equivalent:*

i) *The maximal ideal associated with* x,

$M = \{f \in A : f(x) = 0\}$, *has an approximate identity.*

ii) *There exists a constant* K, *such that for any neighborhood* U *of* x, *any* $\varepsilon > 0$, *there exists* $f \in A$ *with* $\|f\| < K$, $f(x) = 1$, *and* $|f(y)| < \varepsilon$ *for all* $y \in X\backslash U$.

Proof. Suppose M has an approximate identity. Then there exists K such that for any $\varepsilon > 0$, any $f_1, \dots, f_n \in M$, there exists $e \in M$, $\|e\| < K - 1$, $\|ef_j - f_j\| < \varepsilon$. If U is a neighborhood of x, there exist $f_1, \dots, f_n \in M$ such that $\{y : |f_j(y)| < 1, 1 \leq j \leq n\} \subset U$. Choose e accordingly. If $y \notin U$, then for some j, $1 \leq j \leq n$, we have $|f_j(y)| \geq 1$, and $|(ef_j)(y) - f_j(y)| < \varepsilon$; hence $|e(y) - 1| < \varepsilon$ whenever $y \notin U$, and $e(x) = 0$ since $e \in M$. Put $f = 1 - e$. Thus i) implies ii).

If ii) holds, and $f_1, \dots, f_n \in M$, $\varepsilon > 0$, put $U = \{y : |f_j(y)| < \varepsilon/K\}$. Then U is a neighborhood of x. Choose $\delta > 0$ so that $\delta\|f_j\| < \varepsilon$ for $j = 1, \dots, n$, and by ii), choose $f \in A$ with $\|f\| < K$, $f(x) = 1$, $|f(y)| < \delta$ for all $y \notin U$. Put $e = 1 - f$. Then $e \in M$, $\|e\| < K + 1$; for $y \in U$, $|ef_j(y) - f_j(y)| = |f(y)f_j(y)| <$

$\|f\| |f_j(y)| < \varepsilon$, while for $y \notin U$, $|ef_j(y) - f_j(y)| = |f(y)f_j(y)| < \delta\|f_j\| < \varepsilon$. Thus $\|ef_j - f_j\| < \varepsilon$ for $1 \leq j \leq n$. Thus M has an approximate identity. The proof is completed.

COROLLARY 1.6.4. *If* A *is a function algebra on* X, $x \in X$, *and there exists* $f \in A$ *which assumes its maximum modulus only at* x, *then the maximal ideal* $\{f \in A: f(x) = 0\}$ *has an approximate identity.*

Proof. If $f \in A$, $f(x) = 1$ and $|f(y)| < 1$ for $y \neq x$, then for n sufficiently large, f^n satisfies condition ii), with $K = 1$.

THEOREM 1.6.5 (Cohen [1]). *Let* A *be a commutative Banach algebra with unit,* M *a maximal ideal of* A, *and suppose* M *has an approximate identity. Then for every* $f \in M$, *there exist* $g, h \in M$ *such that* $f = gh$. *For any* $\delta > 0$, h *can be chosen in the closed ideal generated by* f, *and* $\|h - f\| < \delta$.

Proof. Let K be as in the definition of approximate identity, and choose c, $0 < c < \frac{1}{4K}$. We can assume $K > 1$. Then $0 < c < \frac{1}{4}$, and it follows that whenever $e \in M$ and $\|e\| \leq K$, we have

$1 - c + ce \in A^{-1}$; indeed,

$$(1 - c + ce)^{-1} = \frac{1}{1 - c} \sum_0^\infty \left(\frac{c}{c - 1}\right)^k e^k,$$

the series converging since $\left\|\frac{ce}{c - 1}\right\| < \frac{1/4}{3/4} = \frac{1}{3}$. Furthermore, if $\|eF - F\|$ is small for some F, then so is $\|EF - F\|$, where $E = (1 - c + ce)^{-1}$. For since $1 = \frac{1}{1 - c} \sum_0^\infty \left(\frac{c}{c - 1}\right)^k$, we have

$$\|EF - F\| = \left\|\frac{1}{1 - c} \sum_0^\infty \left(\frac{c}{c - 1}\right)^k (e^k F - F)\right\|$$

$$\leq \frac{1}{1 - c} \sum_0^\infty \left(\frac{c}{1 - c}\right)^k \|e^k F - F\|,$$

but

$$\|e^k F - F\| = \left\|\sum_0^{k-1} e^{j+1} F - e^j F\right\|$$

$$\leq \sum_0^{k-1} \|e^j\| \|eF - F\|$$

$$\leq \|eF - F\| \sum_0^{k-1} \|e\|^j$$

$$< \|eF - F\| \frac{K^k}{K - 1},$$

hence

$$\|EF - F\| < \|eF - F\| \frac{1}{1 - c} \sum_0^\infty \frac{1}{K - 1} \left[\frac{1}{4(1 - c)}\right]^k$$

$$< \frac{2}{K - 1} \|eF - F\|.$$

This estimate is the key to constructing g and h, which we do as follows.

We shall define inductively a sequence $\{e_n\}$, $e_n \in M$, $\|e_n\| \leq K$, in such a way that if $g_n = c\sum_1^n (1-c)^{k-1} e_k + (1-c)^n$, we have for every n, $g_n \in A^{-1}$, $\|g_n^{-1}f - g_{n+1}^{-1}f\| < \frac{\delta}{2^n}$, and $\|f - g_1^{-1}f\| < \frac{\delta}{2}$. Put $h_n = g_n^{-1}f$. Then $h_n \in M$ (in fact, h_n is in the ideal generated by f) and $\{h_n\}$ is a Cauchy sequence, so $h_n \to h \in M$. Also, $g_n \to c\sum_1^\infty (1-c)^{k-1} e_k = g \in M$ (the series converges since $\|e_k\| \leq K$ and $0 < 1 - c < 1$). Hence, $gh = \lim g_n h_n = \lim g_n g_n^{-1}\mathbf{f} = f$, and the theorem is proved as soon as this construction is made.

Now $g_1 = ce_1 + 1 - c$, so $g_1 \in A^{-1}$ and $\|f - g_1^{-1}f\| < \frac{\delta}{2}$, provided only that $\|e_1 f - f\| < \frac{\delta}{4}(K-1)$. Suppose that $e_1, \ldots, e_n$ have been chosen so that $g_n \in A^{-1}$, etc. We assert that $g_{n+1} \in A^{-1}$ and $\|g_{n+1}^{-1}f - g_n^{-1}f\| < \delta 2^{-n}$ provided only that $\|e_{n+1}f - f\|$ and $\|e_{n+1}e_k - e_k\|$ $(1 \leq k \leq n)$ are sufficiently small. For if $E = (1 - c + ce_{n+1})^{-1}$, we have

$$g_n = E^{-1}c\sum_1^n (1-c)^{k-1} Ee_k + (1-c)^n$$

and

$$g_{n+1} = E^{-1}[c \sum_{1}^{n} (1 - c)^{k-1}Ee_k + (1 - c)^n].$$

Let $G_n = c \sum_{1}^{n} (1 - c)^{k-1}Ee_k + (1 - c)^n$. Then

$$\|G_n - g_n\| < \|Ee_k - e_k\| \, c \sum_{1}^{n} (1 - c)^{k-1}$$

$$< \max_{1 \leq k \leq n} \|Ee_k - e_k\| < \frac{2}{K - 1} \max\|e_{n+1}e_k - e_k\|.$$

Hence $G_n \in A^{-1}$, and $\|G_n^{-1} - g_n^{-1}\|$ is small, provided only that $\|e_{n+1}e_k - e_k\|$ is small for $k = 1, \ldots ,n$. Since $g_{n+1} = E^{-1}G_n$, we have then $g_{n+1} \in A^{-1}$, $g_{n+1}^{-1} = G_n^{-1}E$, so

$$\|g_{n+1}^{-1}f - g_n^{-1}f\| = \|G_n^{-1}EF - g_n^{-1}f\|$$

$$\leq \|G_n^{-1}Ef - g_n^{-1}Ef\| + \|g_n^{-1}Ef - g_n^{-1}f\|$$

$$\leq \|G_n^{-1} - g_n^{-1}\|\|Ef\| + \|g_n^{-1}\|\|Ef - f\|.$$

Thus if $\|e_{n+1}f - f\|$ and $\|e_{n+1}e_k - e_k\| (1 \leq k \leq n)$ are sufficiently small, we will have $\|g_{n+1}^{-1}f - g_n^{-1}f\|$ as small as we please. The inductive construction can thus be accomplished, and the theorem is proved.

We note that the commutativity of A was never used, and that it sufficed that M have a "left approximate identity". See Cohen's paper for the original applications to harmonic analysis, and other factorization results.

COROLLARY 1.6.6. *Let* A *be a commutative Banach algebra with unit,* $\phi \in \text{Spec } A$. *If* $\ker \phi$ *has an approximate identity, then there exists no non-zero point derivation at* ϕ.

This corollary was first pointed out by Curtis and Figá-Talamanca [1]. Combining it with Corollary 1.6.4, we have

COROLLARY 1.6.7. *Let* A *be a function algebra on* X, *let* $x \in X$. *If there exists* $f \in A$ *such that* f *assumes its maximum modulus only at* x, *then there exists no non-zero point derivation at* x.

CHAPTER TWO

MEASURES

2-1 REPRESENTING AND ANNIHILATING MEASURES

Let X be a compact Hausdorff space. By a *measure* on X, we shall understand a complex, regular Borel measure, unless otherwise qualified. A *probability measure* is a positive measure of total mass 1. If μ is a measure, $|\mu|$ denotes the associated positive total variation measure, and we write $\|\mu\|$ for $|\mu|(X)$. For $x \in X$, δ_x denotes the unit point mass at x. For each measure μ on X we can determine a smallest closed set $\operatorname{supp} \mu$ on which μ "lives", its *support*. Thus, $\operatorname{supp} \mu$ is the complement of the union of all open sets U such that $|\mu|(U) = 0$, or equivalently, $x \in \operatorname{supp} \mu$ if and only if $|\mu|(U) > 0$ for every neighborhood U of x.

Our interest in measures derives from the Riesz representation theorem: *if* Φ *is a continuous linear functional on* $C(X)$, *there exists a uniquely determined measure* μ *on* X *such that* $\Phi(f) = \int f d\mu$ *for every* $f \in C(X)$, *and* $\|\mu\| = \|\Phi\|$. Let A be a linear subspace of $C(X)$. Then the Hahn-Banach theorem and the Riesz representation theorem yield the following two remarks:

1) For each $\phi \in A^*$, there exists a measure μ such that $\phi(f) = \int f d\mu$ for all $f \in A$, and $\|\phi\| = \|\mu\|$. Such a μ will be called a *representing measure for* ϕ.

2) The closure of A is precisely the set of all $f \in C(X)$ such that $\int f d\mu = 0$ for every $\mu \in A^\perp$, where $A^\perp = \{\mu : \int g d\mu = 0$ for every $g \in A\}$. The elements of $A^\perp$ will be called annihilating measures for A, and we sometimes write $\mu \perp A$ for $\mu \in A^\perp$.

If μ is a probability measure, the associated linear functional ϕ on $C(X)$ has the property: $\phi(1) = \|\phi\| = 1$. Conversely, but not as obviously, *if* ϕ *is a linear functional on* $C(X)$ *and* $\phi(1) = \|\phi\| = 1$, *the associated measure is a probability measure*. To see this, it suffices to show that $\phi(u) \geq 0$ for every $u \in C(X)$, $0 \leq u \leq 1$. Suppose $\phi(u) = a + ib$, a and b real. For each real t, put $u_t = u + ibt$. Then $\|u_t\|^2 \leq 1 + b^2t^2$, so $|\phi(u_t)|^2 \leq 1 + b^2t^2$, i.e., $a^2 + b^2(t + 1)^2 \leq 1 + b^2t^2$. Thus for all real t, $2tb^2 \leq 1 - a^2 - b^2$, hence $b = 0$. Now $\|1 - u\| \leq 1$, so $|\phi(1) - \phi(u)| \leq 1$, i.e., $|1 - a| \leq 1$, so $a \geq 0$.

If A is a linear subapce of $C(X)$, $1 \in A$, if $\phi \in A^*$ and $\|\phi\| = \phi(1) = 1$, it follows that any representing measure for ϕ is a probability measure. In particular, for each $x \in X$, the associated evaluation functional τ_x, defined by $\tau_x(f) = f(x)$, has the property: $\tau_x \in A^*$, $\tau_x(1) = \|\tau_x\| = 1$, so any representing measure for τ_x is a probability measure. A representing measure for τ_x will also be called a representing measure for x. If A is a function algebra, we see that if $\phi \in \text{Spec } A$, any representing measure for ϕ is a probability measure.

Occasionally we will have use for measures which represent extensions other than Hahn-Banach extensions. If $\phi \in A^*$, we say that the measure

μ represents ϕ, or is a complex representing measure for ϕ, if $\int f d\mu = \phi(f)$ for all $f \in A$. Thus a measure μ which represents ϕ is a representing measure for ϕ if and only if $\|\mu\| = \|\phi\|$. We apologize for this language.

If μ is a measure on X, and $f \in L^1(|\mu|)$, we denote by $f\mu$ the measure corresponding to the linear functional $g \to \int g f d\mu$. Thus, $(f\mu)(E) = \int_E f d\mu$ for every Borel set E. If A is an algebra, then $f\mu \in A^\perp$ whenever $f \in A$ and $\mu \in A^\perp$. Conversely, a closed space A with this property must be an algebra. If A is a function algebra, and μ represents some $\phi \in \text{Spec } A$, then $f\mu \perp A$ whenever $f \in A$ and $\int f d\mu = 0$. These trivial remarks have extensive applications.

Let us look at our standard example, the disk algebra on the circle Γ. Let σ be the normalized Lebesgue measure on Γ. Since $\int z^k d\sigma = 0$ for $k > 0$, it follows that $z\sigma$ is an annihilating measure for A. If $|s| < 1$, and $f \in A$, we can write $f = f(s) + (z - s)g$, where $g \in A$. Put $\nu = \frac{z}{z - s}\sigma$. Then $\int d\nu = \int \sum_0^\infty (s\bar{z})^n d\sigma = \sum_0^\infty s^n \int \bar{z}^n d\sigma = 1$, so $\int f d\nu = f(s) + \int g z d\sigma = f(s)$. Thus ν is a complex measure representing s (the *Cauchy integral formula*). Now $\nu = \frac{1}{1 - s\bar{z}}\sigma$, and $\frac{1}{1 - \bar{s}z} \in A$, so we have for every $f \in A$,

$$\frac{f(s)}{1 - |s|^2} = \int f \frac{1}{1 - \bar{s}z}\,d\nu = \int f \frac{d\sigma}{|1 - s\bar{z}|^2},$$

or

$$f(s) = \int f \frac{1 - |s|^2}{|1 - s\bar{z}|^2}\,d\sigma;$$

i.e., $\frac{1 - |s|^2}{|1 - s\bar{z}|^2}\sigma$ is a (positive) representing measure for s (*Poisson integral formula*). If $f \in A$ and $f(0) = 0$, then $f\sigma \perp A$; such measures are weak-* dense in $A^\perp$, in fact. For if $f \in C(\Gamma)$ and $\int fz^k d\sigma = 0$ for $k \geq 1$, then the Cesaro means of f are polynomials in z, so $f \in A$ by Fejér's theorem. A deeper fact is that the set of measures $f\sigma$, $f \in A$, $f(0) = 0$, is norm dense in $A^\perp$; this is a theorem of F. and M. Riesz, which will be proved in a more general setting in Chapter 4. If $\mu \in A^\perp$ is real, then $\int \bar{z}^k d\mu = 0$ for all $k \geq 0$, as well as $\int z^k d\mu$, so $\mu \perp C(\Gamma)$ by the Fejér (or Weierstrass) theorem, i.e., $\mu = 0$. If $\phi \in A^*$, $\|\phi\| = \phi(1) = 1$, it follows that ϕ admits a *unique* representing measure on Γ, for if λ

and μ represent ϕ, $\lambda - \mu$ is a real annihilating measure, hence 0. In particular, if $|s| < 1$, $\frac{1 - |s|^2}{|1 - s\bar{z}|}\sigma$ is the only representing measure for s on Γ, and for $|s| = 1$, δ_s is the only representing measure for s on Γ. If we look at the disk algebra A on the disk Δ, we find for $|s| < 1$ many other positive measures on Δ representing s, for instance δ_s, or the mean around a circle of center s, or the normalized Lebesgue measure on a disk of center s. But again, if $|s| = 1$, δ_s is the only representing measure for s. For put $g = \frac{1}{2}(1 + \bar{s}z)$. Then $g \in A$, $\|g\| = g(s) = 1$, and $|g(t)| < 1$ for all $t \in \Delta$, $t \neq s$. Then $g^n \in A$ for each positive integer n, and g^n converges boundedly to the characteristic function of $\{s\}$. Hence, if μ is a representing measure for s, $1 = \int g^n d\mu \to \mu(\{s\})$, and since μ is a probability measure, it follows that $\mu = \delta_s$.

As an application of representing measures, we give another proof, due to Hoffman and Singer, of Wermer's maximality theorem (Theorem 1.2.4). Recall the statement: if B is a function algebra on the circle Γ, and $B \supset A$, the disk algebra, then either $B = A$ or $B = C(\Gamma)$. The proof runs as follows. Suppose $\phi(z) \neq 0$ for all $\phi \in \text{Spec } B$. Then $z^{-1} \in B$, and since $z \in B$, $B = C(\Gamma)$ by the Weierstrass (or Fejér) theorem. Suppose on the other hand that there exists $\phi \in \text{Spec } B$ with $\phi(z) = 0$. Then $\phi(f) = f(0)$ for all $f \in A$. If μ is a representing measure for ϕ, it follows that $f(0) = \int f d\mu$ for all $f \in A$, hence, as we have seen, that $\mu = \sigma$, the normalized Lebesgue measure on Γ. Hence for all $f \in B$, we have, for $n \geq 1$, $0 = \phi(z^n)\phi(f) = \phi(z^n f) = \int f z^n d\sigma$. Thus $B \subset A$, so $B = A$. The proof is finished.

The argument by which we derived the Poisson formula from the Cauchy formula can be adapted to a more general context.

THEOREM 2.1.1. *Let* A *be a function algebra on* X, $\phi \in \text{Spec } A$, μ *a complex measure which represents* ϕ. *Then there exists a positive representing measure* σ *for* ϕ, *with* σ *absolutely continuous with respect to* μ.

Proof. Choose a positive measure ρ, and $F \in L^2(\rho)$, such that $\mu = F\rho$ (for example, $\rho = |\mu|$, and $F = \frac{d\mu}{d|\mu|}$). Let H^2 denote the closure of A in $L^2(\rho)$. By the projection theorem in Hilbert space, we may write $\overline{F} = f + g$, where $f \in H^2$ and $g \perp H^2$. Then for every $h \in A$, we have $\phi(h) = \int h d\mu = \int h(\overline{f} + \overline{g}) d\rho = \int h\overline{f} d\rho$. Since $f \in H^2$, there exist $f_n \in A$, $f_n \to f$ in L^2 norm; then for any $h \in A$ with $\phi(h) = 0$, we have $0 = \phi(hf_n) = \int hf_n\overline{f} d\rho$ for all n, and hence $\int h|f|^2 d\rho = 0$. Put $\sigma = c^{-1}|f|^2 \, d\rho$, where $c = \int |f|^2 d\rho$. Then σ is a probability measure, and for all $h \in A$, we have

$$\begin{aligned}\int h d\sigma &= \int [\phi(h) + h - \phi(h)] d\sigma \\ &= \phi(h) + \int [h - \phi(h)] d\sigma = \phi(h),\end{aligned}$$

and the theorem is proved.

The proof above was found by D. Sarason, and independently, by König and perhaps others. The result seems to have been first stated, and a more involved proof given, by Hoffman and Rossi [2].

In the sequel, we shall often deal with the space of all *real-valued* continuous functions on X; we denote it by $C_R(X)$.

2-2 THE CHOQUET BOUNDARY

Throughout this section, we consider a linear subspace A of $C(X)$, X compact Hausdorff, such that A separates the points of X and contains the constants. We set

$$K = \{\phi \in A^* : \phi(1) = \|\phi\| = 1\}.$$

It is clear that K is a convex subset of the closed unit ball of A^*, containing each τ_x $(x \in X)$, and that K is weak-* closed, hence weak-* compact.

DEFINITION. The *Choquet boundary* of A, denoted $Ch(A)$, is the set of all $x \in X$ such that τ_x admits a unique representing measure; i.e., such that δ_x is the only representing measure for τ_x.

If $x \notin Ch(A)$, *there exists a representing measure* μ *for* τ_x *with* $\mu(\{x\}) = 0$. For if ν is a representing measure for $\tau_x, \nu \neq \delta_x$, then $\nu(\{x\}) = c < 1$. Put $\mu = (1 - c)^{-1}(\nu - c\delta_x)$. It is trivial to verify that μ is a positive measure which represents τ_x, and $\mu(\{x\}) = 0$.

THEOREM 2.2.1. *Let* $x \in X$. *Suppose there exist constants* α, β, *with* $0 < \alpha < \beta < 1$, *such that for every neighborhood* U *of* x *there exists* $f \in A$ *with* $\|f\| \leq 1$, $f(x) > \beta$, *and* $|f(y)| < \alpha$ *for all* $y \notin U$. *Then* $x \in Ch(A)$.

<u>Proof</u>. Let μ be a representing measure for τ_x, and U a neighborhood of x. Then for some $f \in A$,

$$\beta < f(x) = \int f d\mu = \int_U f d\mu + \int_{X\setminus U} f d\mu$$

$$\leq \mu(U) + \alpha\mu(X\setminus U) = \alpha + (1 - \alpha)\mu(U).$$

Thus $\mu(U) > \frac{\beta - \alpha}{1 - \alpha}$ for any neighborhood U of x, so $\mu(\{x\}) \geq \frac{\beta - \alpha}{1 - \alpha}$. The theorem follows from the remark above.

The same sort of result holds if we consider real parts.

THEOREM 2.2.2. *Let* $x \in X$. *Suppose there exist* α, β, *with* $0 < \alpha < \beta$, *such that for every neighborhood* U *of* x *there exists* $f \in A$ *with* $\text{Re} f \leq 0$, $\text{Re} f(x) > -\alpha$, *and* $\text{Re} f(y) < -\beta$ *for* $y \notin U$. *Then* $x \in Ch(A)$.

Proof. From $-\alpha < \text{Re}f(x) = \int \text{Re}f d\mu < -\beta\mu(X\setminus U)$, we find $\mu(U) > \frac{\beta - \alpha}{\beta}$ for any representing measure μ for x, any neighborhood U of x, and the theorem follows as before.

THEOREM 2.2.3. *Let* $\phi \in K$, $u \in C_R(X)$. *Let*

$$\alpha = \sup\{ \text{Re}\phi(f) : f \in A, \text{Re}f \leq u\} \text{ and}$$
$$\beta = \inf\{ \text{Re}\phi(f) : f \in A, \text{Re}f \geq u\},$$

so $\alpha \leq \beta$. *For any* γ, $\alpha \leq \gamma \leq \beta$, *there exists a representing measure* μ *for* ϕ *with* $\int u d\mu = \gamma$.

Proof. Replacing u by $u - \gamma$, we may assume that $\gamma = 0$. Let $N = \{f \in C(X) : \text{Re}f \leq tu + \text{Re}g$ for some real t, some $g \in A$ with $\text{Re}\phi(g) \leq 0\}$, and let $P = \{f \in C(X) : \text{Re}f > 0\}$. It is clear that N and P are convex cones, and P is open. Also, N and P are disjoint, for if $tu + \text{Re}g > 0$, t real, $g \in A$, then $\text{Re}\phi(g) > -t\alpha \geq 0$ if $t > 0$, and $\text{Re}\phi(g) > |t|\beta \geq 0$ if $t < 0$. Hence, by the separation theorem, there exists a non-zero $\Phi \in C(X)^*$ with $\text{Re}\Phi(f) \leq 0$ for $f \in N$, $\text{Re}\Phi(f) \geq 0$ for $f \in P$. The latter inequality easily implies that Φ is a positive linear functional, so we may assume also that $\Phi(1) = 1$. If $f \in A$, $\pm(f - \mathrm{Re}\phi(f)) \in N$, so $\mathrm{Re}\Phi(f) = \mathrm{Re}\phi(f)$. Since $\mathrm{Im}\theta(f) = \mathrm{Re}\theta(-if)$ for any linear functional θ, it follows that $\Phi(f) = \phi(f)$ for any $f \in A$. Since $\pm u \in N$, $\Phi(u) = 0$. Take μ to be the measure which represents Φ. The proof is finished.

COROLLARY 2.2.4. *Let* $\phi \in K$. *Then* ϕ *admits a unique representing measure* μ *if and only if for every* $u \in C_R(X)$,

$$\sup\{\mathrm{Re}\phi(f) : f \in A, \mathrm{Re} f \leq u\} = \int u d\mu.$$

COROLLARY 2.2.5. *Let* $x \in X$. *Then* $x \in Ch(A)$ *if and only if for every* $u \in C_R(X)$,

$$\sup\{\mathrm{Re} f(x) : f \in A, \mathrm{Re} f \leq u\} = u(x).$$

Combining this last Corollary with Theorem 2.2.2, we obtain the following characterization of $Ch(A)$:

THEOREM 2.2.6. *The following statements are equivalent:*

i) *For every* $\alpha, \beta, 0 < \alpha < \beta$, *and every neighborhood* U *of* x, *there exists* $f \in A$, *with*

Ref ≤ 0, Ref$(x) > -\alpha$, *and* Ref$(y) < -\beta$ *for all* $y \notin U$.

ii) *There exist* $\alpha, \beta, 0 < \alpha < \beta$, *such that for every neighborhood* U *of* x *there exists* $f \in A$, *with* Ref ≤ 0, Ref$(x) > -\alpha$, Ref$(y) < -\beta$ *for all* $y \notin U$.

iii) $x \in Ch(A)$.

Proof. That i) implies ii) is trivial, and ii) implies iii) is Theorem 2.2.2. Suppose $x \in Ch(A)$, U a neighborhood of x, $0 < \alpha < \beta$. By Urysohn's lemma, there exists $u \in C_R(X)$, $u \leq 0$, $u(x) = 0$, and $u < -\beta$ on $X \backslash U$. By Corollary 2.2.5, there exists $f \in A$ with Ref $\leq u$ and Ref$(x) > -\alpha$. Thus iii) implies i), and all is proved.

COROLLARY 2.2.7. *If* X *is metrizeable, then* $Ch(A)$ *is a* G_δ *(countable intersection of open sets).*

Proof. Let ρ be a metric on X inducing the topology of X. For each positive integer n, let G_n be the set of all $x \in X$ for which there exists $f \in A$ with Ref ≤ 0, Ref$(x) > -1$, and Ref$(y) < -2$ for all y with $\rho(x,y) \geq 1/n$. It is clear that each G_n is open, and $Ch(A) = \bigcap_1^\infty G_n$ by Theorem 2.2.6.

If X is not assumed metrizeable then, $Ch(A)$ need not even be a Borel set. See Bishop and deLeeuw [1] for examples.

THEOREM 2.2.8. *Let* $\phi \in K$. *Then* ϕ *is an extreme point of* K *if and only if* $\phi = \tau_x$ *for some* $x \in Ch(A)$.

<u>Proof</u>. Let $x \in Ch(A)$, and suppose $\tau_x = t\phi + (1 - t)\psi$, where $\phi, \psi \in K$ and $0 < t < 1$. Let μ, ν be representing measures for ϕ, ψ respectively. Then $t\mu + (1 - t)\nu$ is a representing measure for τ_x, and since $x \in Ch(A)$, $\delta_x = t\mu + (1 - t)\nu$. Since μ and ν are positive measures, it follows that $\mu(E) = \nu(E) = 0$ whenever E a Borel set, $x \notin E$, and so $\mu = \nu = \delta_x$, and hence $\phi = \psi = \tau_x$. Thus τ_x is extreme.

Now suppose that ϕ is an extreme point of K. Let μ be a representing measure for ϕ, and let $x \in \operatorname{supp} \mu$, so $\mu(U) > 0$ for every neighborhood U of x. If for some neighborhood U of x, $\mu(U) < 1$, define θ and ψ by

$$\theta(f) = \frac{1}{\mu(U)} \int_U f d\mu,$$

$$\psi(f) = (1 - \mu(U))^{-1} \int_{X \setminus U} f d\mu;$$

then $\theta, \psi \in K$, and $\phi = \mu(U)\theta + (1 - \mu(U))\psi$. Since ϕ is an extreme point of K, it follows that $\theta = \psi = \phi$, i.e., that $\phi(f) = \mu(U)^{-1}\int_U f d\mu$. But if $\mu(U) < 1$ for some neighborhood U of x, then $\mu(V) < 1$ for any smaller neighborhood V, so $\phi(f) = \mu(V)^{-1}\int_V f d\mu$ for any $f \in A$, and arbitrarily small neighborhoods V of x. It follows that $\phi = \tau_x$. Since x was an arbitrary point of supp μ, and A separates points, it follows that supp $\mu = \{x\}$, and $\mu = \delta_x$. If $\mu(U) = 1$ for every neighborhood U of x, we have at once that $\mu = \delta_x$. Since μ was an arbitrary representing measure for ϕ, it follows that $\phi = \tau_x$, with $x \in Ch(A)$, and the proof is concluded.

The Krein-Milman theorem now assures us that $Ch(A)$ is not empty.

DEFINITION. A subset Y of X is called a *boundary* for A if for every $f \in A$ there exists

$y \in Y$ such that $|f(y)| = \|f\|$.

THEOREM 2.2.9. *The Choquet boundary is a boundary.*

Proof. Let $f \in A$, and let $x \in X$ be any point where $|f(x)| = \|f\|$. Put $L = \{\phi \in K : \phi(f) = f(x)\}$. Clearly, L is a closed convex subset of K, L is not empty since $\tau_x \in L$, so by the Krein-Milman theorem there exists an extreme point ϕ of L. But then ϕ is extreme in K: for if $\phi = t\theta + (1 - t)\psi$, $\theta, \psi \in K$, we have

$$\|f\| = |\phi(f)| \leq t|\theta(f)| + (1 - t)|\psi(f)| \leq \|f\|,$$

so equality holds, so $\theta(f) = \psi(f) = \phi(f)$, i.e., $\theta, \psi \in L$, and since ϕ is extreme in L, $\theta = \psi = \phi$. By Theorem 2.2.8, $\phi = \tau_y$ for some $y \in Ch(A)$, and the proof is finished.

COROLLARY 2.2.10. *The closure of the Choquet boundary is a closed boundary, contained in every closed boundary.*

Proof. If Y is a closed boundary for A, it is clear that the restriction map is an isometry of A onto $A|K = \{f|K : f \in A\}$. Hence, each $\phi \in K$ admits a representing measure whose support is contained in Y; it follows immediately that $Y \supset Ch(A)$.

The unique minimal closed boundary is called the *Shilov boundary*; its existence (for algebras of functions) was first proved by Shilov. Other proofs have been given by Arens and Singer [1], and Hörmander [1], among others. Hörmander's proof does not use the axiom of choice.

The main theorem about the Choquet boundary is Choquet's Theorem: *if* X *is metrizeable, then for each* $\phi \in K$, *there exists a representing measure* μ *which is concentrated on the Choquet boundary, in the sense that* $\mu(X \backslash Ch(A)) = 0$. A beautiful short proof of this theorem was found (independently) by Bonsall [1] and Hervé [1]. If X is not metrizeable, the situation is more complicated; since Ch(A) need not be a Borel set, the statement of the theorem must be modified. The generalization of Choquet's theorem to the non-metrizeable case is due to Bishop and deLeeuw [1]. The reader is referred to the book of Phelps [1] for a more complete discussion and further references.

2-3 PEAK POINTS

Throughout this section, A will be a *closed* subspace of C(X), X compact Hausdorff, separating the points of X and containing the constant functions.

DEFINITION. A subset K of X is said to be a *peak set* if there exists $f \in A$ such that

$$K = \{x \in X : f(x) = 1\}$$
$$= \{x \in X : |f(x)| = \|f\|\};$$

any such f is said to *peak on* K. We call K a *peak set in the weak sense* if K is the intersection of some collection of peak sets. A point $x \in X$ is called a *peak point* if $\{x\}$ is a peak set, or a *peak point in the weak sense* if $\{x\}$ is a peak set in the weak sense. Peak points in the weak sense are also referred to as *strong boundary points*.

We note that a peak set is necessarily a compact G_δ $(K = \bigcap_1^\infty \{x \in X : |f(x)| > 1 - \frac{1}{n}\})$, and peak sets in the weak sense are compact.

LEMMA 2.3.1. *If the closed subset* K *of* X *is a peak set in the weak sense and a* G_δ, *then* K *is a peak set. In particular, the intersection of a countable family of peak sets is a peak set.*

Proof. Suppose $K = \bigcap_1^\infty G_n$, each G_n open, and $K = \bigcap_{\alpha \in I} K_\alpha$, where K_α is a peak set for each α in the index set I. By the finite intersection principle, for each n there exists $\alpha_n \in I$ with $K_{\alpha_n} \subset G_n$. Let $f_n \in A$ peak on K_{α_n}; then $f = \sum_1^\infty 2^{-n} f_n$ $\in A$, since A is uniformly closed, and f evidently peaks on $\bigcap_1^\infty K_{\alpha_n} = K$.

In particular, if X is metrizeable, there is no distinction between peak sets (or peak points) in the weak sense and peak sets (or peak points).

THEOREM 2.3.2 (Bishop [2]). *Suppose* $x \in X$, *and suppose that for every neighborhood* U *of* x *there exists* $f \in A$ *such that* $\|f\| \leq 1$, $f(x) > \frac{3}{4}$, *and* $|f(y)| < \frac{1}{4}$ *for all* $y \notin U$. *Then* x *is a peak point in the weak sense.*

Proof. We must show that for every neighborhood V of x there exists a peak set K with $x \in K \subset V$. Now our hypothesis may be restated: for every neighborhood U of x there exists $f_U \in A$, with

$f_U(x) = 1$, $\|f_U\| < \frac{4}{3}$, and $|f_U(y)| < \frac{1}{3}$ for all $y \notin U$. We define inductively a sequence $\{U_n\}$ of neighborhoods of x, and a sequence $\{f_n\}$ in A, as follows: let $U_1 = V$, and $f_1 = f_V$. Having defined $U_1, \ldots, U_{n-1}$ and $f_1, \ldots, f_{n-1}$, set

$$U_n = \{y \in U_{n-1} : |f_j(y)| < 1 + \frac{1}{3} 2^{-n},\quad 1 \leq j \leq n - 1\},$$

and put $f_n = f_{U_n}$. Now let $f = \sum_1^\infty 2^{-n} f_n$, and $K = \{y \in X : f(y) = 1\}$.

If $y \notin V = U_1 = \bigcup_1^\infty U_n$, we have $|f_n(y)| < \frac{1}{3}$ for all n, so $|f(y)| < \frac{1}{3}$. If for some n, $y \in U_n \setminus U_{n+1}$, we have $|f_j(y)| < 1 + \frac{1}{3} 2^{-n}$ for $1 \leq j < n$, and $|f_j(y)| < \frac{1}{3}$ for all $j > n$, so

$$|f(y)| < \sum_{j=1}^{n-1} (1 + \frac{1}{3} 2^{-n}) 2^{-j} + \frac{4}{3} 2^{-n} + \frac{1}{3} \sum_{n+1}^{\infty} 2^{-j}$$

$$= (1 + \frac{1}{3} 2^{-n})(1 - 2^{1-n}) + (\frac{4}{3} + \frac{1}{3}) 2^{-n}$$

$$= 1 - \frac{2}{3} 4^{-n} < 1.$$

Finally, if $y \in \bigcap_1^\infty U_n$, then $|f_j(y)| < 1 + \frac{1}{3} 2^{-n}$ for all $n > j$, so $|f_j(y)| \leq 1$ for all j, so $|f(y)| \leq 1$. Thus $\|f\| \leq 1$, $f(x) = 1$, and $|f(y)| < 1$ for all

$y \notin \bigcap_1^\infty U_n$. In particular, $K \subset V$, and $\frac{1}{2}(1 + f)$ peaks on K. The theorem is proved.

LEMMA 2.3.3. *If* $x \in X$ *is a peak point in the weak sense, then* x *belongs to the Choquet boundary.*

Proof. Let μ be a representing measure for x, and U any neighborhood of x. There exists $f \in A$ which peaks on K, $x \in K \subset U$. Then $0 = \int (1 - f)d\mu = \int \mathrm{Re}(1 - f)d\mu$, but $\mathrm{Re}(1 - f) > 0$ outside U, so $\mu(X\backslash U) = 0$. It now follows from the regularity of μ that $\mu(X\backslash\{x\}) = 0$, i.e., that $\mu = \delta_x$. This proves the lemma.

We now return our attention to function algebras. Gathering together the results of this section and the last, we have:

THEOREM 2.3.4. *Let* A *be a function algebra on* X, $x \in X$. *Then the following are equivalent:*

i) x *is a peak point in the weak sense;*

ii) $x \in Ch(A)$;

ii') *If* μ *is a representing measure for* x, $\mu(\{x\}) > 0$;

iii) *There exist* α, β, *with* $0 < \alpha < \beta < 1$, *such that for any neighborhood* U *of* x *there exists* $f \in A$, $\|f\| \leq 1$, $f(x) > \beta$, *and* $|f(y)| < \alpha$ *for all* $y \notin U$.

Proof. i) implies ii) is Lemma 2.3.3; ii) and ii') are equivalent by the remark made immediately following the definition of Choquet boundary; iii) implies ii) is Theorem 2.2.1. If iii) holds with $\alpha = \frac{1}{4}$, $\beta = \frac{3}{4}$, then i) holds by Theorem 2.3.2. We now use the hypothesis that A is an algebra to show that ii) implies iii) with any α, β (in particular, $\frac{1}{4}$, $\frac{3}{4}$). If $x \in Ch(A)$, by Theorem 2.2.6, for any $0 < \alpha < \beta < 1$, any neighborhood U of x, there exists $g \in A$, with $\operatorname{Re} g \leq 0$, $\operatorname{Re} g(x) > \log \beta$, and $\operatorname{Re} g(y) < \log \alpha$ for all $y \notin U$. Since A is a function algebra, $\exp g = f \in A$. All is proven.

THEOREM 2.3.5. *Let* A *be a function algebra on* X, *and suppose* X *is metrizeable. Then the set of all peak points for* A *is a boundary for* A, *and a* G_δ *set.*

Proof. By Theorem 2.3.4 (and the remark following Lemma 2.3.1), the set of peak points coincides with the Choquet boundary, which is a boundary by Theorem 2.2.9, and a G_δ by Corollary 2.2.7.

Since any boundary must certainly contain

every peak point, under the hypothesis of Theorem 2.3.5 we see that *the set of peak points is the unique minimal boundary for* A, *contained in every boundary*. If X is not metrizeable, there need not exist such a smallest boundary. For instance, let $X = \prod_{\alpha \in I} I_\alpha$, where each I_α, as well as the index set I, is the interval [0,1]. Let $K = \{x \in X : x_\alpha = 0$ for all but countably many α's$\}$, $L = \{x \in X : x_\alpha = 1$ for all but countably many α's$\}$. Then K and L are disjoint, but each is a boundary for C(X), since one sees from the Stone-Weierstrass theorem that each $f \in C(X)$ depends on only countably many coordinates.

We close this section with a few remarks. We can now rephrase a result of Chapter 1 (Lemma 1.6.3): *if* A *is a function algebra on* X, $x \in X$, *the maximal ideal associated with* x *has an approximate identity if and only if* x *is a peak point in the weak sense.*

If A = C(X), it is clear that each point of X is a peak point in the weak sense for A. For a long time, it was conjectured that if A is a function algebra on X, with Spec A = X, and if each point of X is a peak point for A (or more generally, if Ch(A) = X), then A = C(X). This "peak point conjecture" was recently smashed (along with other conjectures) by Brian Cole [1]. We describe one of Cole's examples in the Appendix.

It is sometimes useful to observe that if A is a function algebra on X, a stronger version of Lemma 2.3.3 holds: *if* x *is a peak point in the weak sense, and* μ *any (complex) measure representing* x, *then* $\mu(\{x\}) = 1$. For if U any neighborhood of x, there exists f ∈ A which peaks on K, $x \in K \subset U$. Then $1 = f^n(x) = \int f^n d\mu$ for all n, and f^n converges boundedly to χ_K, so $\mu(K) = 1$, and the result follows from the regularity of μ.

2-4 PEAK SETS AND INTERPOLATION

Throughout this section, A will be a function algebra on X. We begin with a theorem of Bishop.

THEOREM 2.4.1. *Suppose* K *is a peak set for* A, *and* g ∈ A *does not vanish on* K. *Then there exists* f ∈ A *such that* $f|K = g|K$, *and* $|f(x)| < \|f\|$ *for every* $x \in X\backslash K$.

Proof. Without loss of generality, we may assume $\|g\|_K = 1$. Let h be a function in A which peaks on

K, so $h(x) = 1$ for $x \in K$, $|h(x)| < 1$ for $x \in X \setminus K$. For each positive integer n, let

$$U_n = \{x \in X : |g(x)| < 1 + 2^{-n}\}.$$

Thus each U_n is an open neighborhood of K, and $U_{n+1} \subset U_n$ for every n. Let $M = \| g \|$, and choose for each n a positive integer k_n such that $|h^{k_n}(x)| < 2^{-n}M^{-1}$ for all $x \in X \setminus U_n$. Put $f = g \sum_1^\infty 2^{-n} h^{k_n}$. It is clear that $f \in A$ and that $f|K = g|K$. It remains to verify that $|f(x)| < 1$ whenever $x \in X \setminus K$. If $x \in X \setminus U_1$, then $|h^{k_n}(x)| < M^{-1}2^{-n}$ for every n, and so $|f(x)| \le |g(x)| \Sigma 2^{-n} |h^{k_n}(x)| \le MM^{-1}\Sigma 2^{-2n} = \frac{1}{3} < 1$. If for some n, $x \in U_n \setminus U_{n+1}$, then $|g(x)| < 1 + 2^{-n}$, and $|h^{k_j}(x)| < M^{-1}2^{-j}$ for all $j > n$, so

$$\begin{aligned} |f(x)| &< (1 + 2^{-n}) \sum_1^n 2^{-j} + M \sum_{n+1}^\infty M^{-1}2^{-2j} \\ &= (1 + 2^{-n})(1 - 2^{-n}) + \frac{1}{3} 4^{-n} \\ &= 1 - 4^{-n} + \frac{1}{3} 4^{-n} < 1. \end{aligned}$$

Finally, if $x \in \bigcap_1^\infty U_n$, and $x \in X \setminus K$, then $|g(x)| \le 1$ and $|h(x)| < 1$, so $|f(x)| < 1$. The proof is finished.

If K is assumed to be only a peak set in the

weak sense, we have a similar result.

THEOREM 2.4.2. *Let* K *be a peak set in the weak sense, and let* $g \in A$, $g|K \neq 0$. *If* L *is any* G_δ *set containing* K, *there exists* $f \in A$ *with* $f|K = g|K$, *such that* $|f(x)| < \|f\|$ *for every* $x \in X \setminus L$.

Proof. Let $L' = \{x \in X : |g(x)| \leq \|g\|_K\}$. Then L' is a G_δ containing K. We can find a peak set K' with $K \subset K' \subset L \cap L'$, and the theorem follows by applying Theorem 2.41 to K'.

COROLLARY 2.4.3. *Let* K *be a peak set in the weak sense. Then* $A|K$ *is closed.*

Proof. Suppose g is in the closure of $A|K$. Then there exist $g_n \in A$ such that $\|g_n - g\|_K < 2^{-n}$. By Theorem 2.4.2, we can find $f_n \in A$ with $\|f_n\| < 2^{-n+1}$ and $f_n|K = (g_{n+1} - g_n)|K$. Then $f = \sum_1^\infty f_n \in A$, and $f|K = \lim(g_n - g_1)|K = g - g_1|K$, so $g = (f + g_1)|K \in A|K$, completing the proof.

COROLLARY 2.4.4. *If* K *is a peak set for* A, *and* $L \subset K$ *is a peak set for* $A|K$, *then* L *is a peak set for* A. *The same holds with "peak set" replaced throughout by "peak set in the weak sense".*

Proof. Obvious from Theorem 2.4.1 (or 2.4.2).

COROLLARY 2.4.5. *If* K *is a peak set (in the weak sense) containing more than one point, there exists a proper subset* L *of* K *which is a peak set (in the weak sense).*

Proof. Since A separates points, there exists $g \in A$ which is not constant on K. We can assume $\|g\|_K = 1$ and $g(x) = 1$ for some $x \in K$. Then $L = \{x \in K : g(x) = 1\}$ is a peak set for $A|K$ ($\frac{1}{2}(1 + g)$ peaks on L, relative to K), and the Corollary now follows from Corollary 2.4.4.

COROLLARY 2.4.6. *Every peak set contains a peak point in the weak sense.*

Proof. Ordering the peak sets in the weak sense by inclusion, it follows at once from Zorn's lemma that every peak set contains a minimal peak set in the weak sense. By Corollary 2.4.5, a minimal peak set in the weak sense must be a singleton.

This last result yields another proof of the fact that the set of peak points in the weak sense is a boundary, and thus in the case that X satisfies the first axiom of countability, that the set of peak points is a boundary. For if $f \in A$, $K = \{x : |f(x)| = \|f\|\}$ contains a peak set: namely, choose any $x \in K$, then $(2\|f\|)^{-1}(1 + \overline{\operatorname{sgn} f(x)} f)$ peaks on $\{y \in K : f(y) = f(x)\}$. Then K contains, by Corollary 2.4.6, a peak point in the weak sense, which was the assertion. This is Bishop's original proof, given in [2].

We now turn our attention to the relationship between peak sets in the weak sense and annihilating measures.

THEOREM 2.4.7. *Let* K *be a peak set in the weak sense. Then* $\chi_K \mu \in A^\perp$ *whenever* $\mu \in A^\perp$.

Proof. If $\mu \in A^\perp$, and $\varepsilon > 0$, we can find a neighborhood U of K such that $|\mu|(U|K) < \varepsilon$. There exists a peak set L with $K \subset L \subset U$. If f peaks on L, then $f^n \to \chi_L$ pointwise and boundedly, so by Lebesgue's dominated convergence theorem we have for every $g \in A$,

$$\int g\chi_L d\mu = \lim \int g f^n d\mu = 0.$$

But $|\int g\chi_K d\mu - \int g\chi_L d\mu| \leq |\mu|(L\setminus K)\|g\| < \varepsilon\|g\|$. Since ε was arbitrary, $\int g\chi_K d\mu = 0$ for all $g \in A$, which was to be proved.

This result can be used to give another proof of Corollary 2.4.3. Let T be the restriction mapping, $Tf = f|K$, of A into the closure of $A|K$. We want to show that T has closed range; by a standard result of functional analysis, this will be the case if (and only if) the adjoint map T^* has closed range. Let $\phi \in (A|K)^*$, let μ be a Hahn-Banach extension of ϕ to $C(K)$. Then

$$\|\phi\| = \|\mu\| = \inf\{\|\mu + \nu\| : \nu \in A^\perp,\ \text{supp}\ \nu \subset K\},$$

and $\|T^*\phi\| = \inf\{ \mu + \nu \ : \nu \in A^\perp\}$, as we see by considering a Hahn-Banach extension of $T^*\phi$ to $C(X)$. (This is the hopefully familiar argument that A^* is isometrically isomorphic to $C(X)^*/A^\perp$). But if $\nu \in A^\perp$, $\|\mu + \nu\| = \|\mu + \chi_K\nu + (1 - \chi_K)\nu\| \geq \|\mu + \chi_K\nu\|$, and $\chi_K\nu \in A^\perp$ by Theorem 2.4.7. Thus T^* is an isometry, hence has closed range, and the proof is completed.

For the proof of the converse to Theorem 2.4.7, we shall need a lemma from functional analysis.

LEMMA 2.4.8. *Let* C *be a Banach space, and let* S *and* T *be weak-* closed subspaces of* C^*. *Then* $S + T$ *is weak-* closed if (and only if) there exists a constant* k *such that for each* $\lambda \in S + T$ *there exist* $\mu \in S$, $\nu \in T$ *with* $\lambda = \mu + \nu$ *and* $\|\mu\| \leq k\|\lambda\|$.

Proof. Let $E = \{\mu \in S : \|\mu\| \leq k\}$ and $F = \{\nu \in T : \|\nu\| \leq 1 + k\}$. Since S and T are weak-* closed, E and F are weak-* compact, by the Banach-Alaoglu theorem. Since the map $(\mu, \nu) \to \mu + \nu$ is continuous, and $E \times F$ is compact, it follows that $\{\mu + \nu : \mu \in E, \nu \in F\}$ is weak-* compact; but by hypothesis, this set contains the closed unit ball of S + T. Thus the closed unit ball of S + T is weak-* compact, and the theorem of Banach-Krein-Smulian now assures us that S + T is weak-* closed.

The "only if" part of the lemma follows from the open mapping theorem, since weak-* closed subspaces are norm closed.

The next theorem is due to Glicksberg [1].

THEOREM 2.4.9. *Let* K *be a closed subset of* X *with the property that* $\chi_K\mu \in A^\perp$ *whenever* $\mu \in A^\perp$. *Then* K *is a peak set in the weak sense.*

Proof. Let Y be the space obtained from X by identifying K to a point y_0, and let π be the canonical map of X onto Y; thus π maps $X\backslash K$ homeomorphically onto $Y\backslash\{y_0\}$, and $\pi(K) = y_0$. Let $B' = \{f \in C(Y) : f\circ\pi \in A\}$, $B = \{f\circ\pi : f \in B'\}$. Thus $f \in B$ if and only if $f \in A$ and $f|K$ is constant. Let M(K) be the set of all measures μ on X such that supp $\mu \subset K$ and $\mu(K) = 0$. Then $A^{\perp} + M(K)$ is weak-* dense in $B^{\perp}$. Now if $\mu \in A^{\perp}$, $\nu \in M(K)$, then $\mu + \nu = (1 - \chi_K)\mu + \chi_K\mu + \nu$, and $(1 - \chi_K)\mu \in A^{\perp}$ and $\chi_K\mu + \nu \in M(K)$ by hypothesis. Since $\|\mu + \nu\| = \|(1 - \chi_K)\mu\| + \|\chi_K\mu + \nu\|$, Lemma 2.4.8 applies, with $C = C(X)$, $S = A^{\perp}$, $T = M(K)$, and $k = 1$. Thus $A^{\perp} + M(K)$ is weak-* closed, and hence $B^{\perp} = A^{\perp} + M(K)$.

We next observe that B' is a function algebra on Y. The only point to check is that B' separates the points of Y, i.e., that $\delta_{\pi x} - \delta_{\pi y} \perp B'$ only if $\pi x = \pi y$. If μ is a measure on X, let $\pi\mu$ denote the induced measure on Y: thus $\int fd(\pi\mu) = \int f\circ\pi \, d\mu$ for all $f \in C(Y)$. Then $\mu \perp B$ if and only if $\pi\mu \perp B'$. If $\delta_{\pi x} - \delta_{\pi y} \perp B'$, then $\delta_x - \delta_y \in B^{\perp}$ (since $\delta_{\pi x} = \pi\delta_x$), so $\delta_x - \delta_y = \mu + \nu$, where $\mu \in A^{\perp}$, $\nu \in M(K)$. Then $(\delta_x - \delta_y)(K) = 0$, so either $\{x, y\} \subset X\backslash K$ or $\{x, y\} \subset K$. If $\{x, y\} \subset X\backslash K$, then $\delta_x - \delta_y = (1 - \chi_K)\mu \in A^{\perp}$, and since A separates points, $x = y$. If $\{x, y\} \subset K$, then $\pi x = \pi y = y_0$. Thus B' separates points.

Next we show that y_0 is a peak point in the weak sense for B'. It suffices (Theorem 2.3.4) to show that there exists no representing measure σ

for y_0 with $\sigma(\{y_0\}) = 0$. Suppose σ were such a measure; then $\sigma = \pi\rho$, where ρ is defined by $\rho(E) = \sigma(\pi(E\backslash K))$ for Borel sets E in X. Since $\delta_{y_0} - \sigma \perp B'$, it follows that $\delta_x - \rho \in B^\perp$ for any $x \in K$, whence $\delta_x - \rho = \mu + \nu$ for some $\mu \in A^\perp$, $\nu \in M(K)$. Since $\rho(K) = \mu(K) = \nu(K) = 0$, we reach the contradiction that $\delta_x(K) = 0$. Thus no such σ can exist, and y_0 is a peak point in the weak sense for B'. It is immediate that then K is a peak set in the weak sense for A, and the proof is concluded.

As an application, we have the following interpolation theorem, due to Bishop [4].

THEOREM 2.4.10. *Let* K *be a closed* G_δ *subset of* X. *Then the following two conditions are equivalent.*

i) *for every* $g \in C(K)$, $g \neq 0$, *there exists* $f \in A$ *such that* $f|K = g$, *and* $|f(x)| < \|f\|$ *for all* $x \in X\backslash K$;

ii) *for every* $\mu \in A^\perp$, $|\mu|(K) = 0$.

Proof. Suppose i) holds. Taking $g = 1$, we see that K is a peak set, so by Theorem 2.4.7 $\chi_K\mu \in A^\perp$ for every $\mu \in A^\perp$. Hence, if $\mu \in A^\perp$ $\int_K g\,d\mu = 0$ for every $g \in C(K)$, so $|\mu|(K) = 0$.

Now suppose ii) holds. Then $\chi_K\mu = 0$ for every

$\mu \in A^{\perp}$, so K is a peak set in the weak sense by Theorem 2.4.9, and since K is a G_δ, it follows that K is a peak set. Hence $A|K$ is closed (Corollary 2.4.3), and since $A|K$ is evidently dense in $C(K)$, we have $A|K = C(K)$. The remaining assertion of i) now comes from Theorem 2.4.1, and the proof is finished.

Sets with property i) are sometimes called *peak interpolation sets*. The reader may formulate the corresponding notion of peak interpolation sets in the weak sense, and prove the corresponding theorem.

Theorem 2.4.10 is a generalization of the following "classical" result, found independently by Rudin and Carleson:

Let A *be the disk algebra, and* K *a closed subset of the unit circle with Lebesgue measure* 0. *Then for every* $g \in C(K)$ *there exists* $f \in A$ *whose restriction to* K *is* g, *and which assumes its maximum modulus only on* K.

The proof consists of noting that $|\mu|(K) = 0$ for every $\mu \in A^{\perp}$, by the F. and M. Riesz theorem, and applying Theorem 2.4.10.

The argument used in the second proof of

Corollary 2.4.3 yields a result parallel to Theorem 2.4.10.

THEOREM 2.4.11. *Let* A *be a closed linear subspace of* C(X), K *a closed subset of* X. *Then the following two conditions are equivalent*:

i) *for every* $g \in C(K)$, *and every* $\varepsilon > 0$, *there exists* $f \in A$ *such that* $f|K = g$, *and* $\|f\| < (1 + \varepsilon)\|g\|$;

ii) *for every* $\mu \in A^{\perp}$, $|\mu|(X\backslash K) \geq |\mu|(K)$.

Proof. Let T be the restriction map of A into C(K). Then for any measure λ on K, $T^*\lambda$ is the linear functional on A given by $f \to \int f d\lambda$, and so from the Hahn-Banach theorem, $\|T^*\lambda\| = \inf\{\|\lambda + \mu\|: \mu \in A^{\perp}\}$. Thus T^* is an isometry if and only if $\|\lambda\| \leq \|\lambda + \mu\|$ for all measures λ on K, all $\mu \in A^{\perp}$. Taking $\lambda = -\chi_K\mu$, we find that if T^* is an isometry, then $\|\chi_K\mu\| \leq \|(1 - \chi_K)\mu\|$ for all $\mu \in A^{\perp}$, i.e., ii) holds. On the other hand, if ii) holds, then for any λ supported on K and any $\mu \in A^{\perp}$, we have

$$\begin{aligned}\|\lambda + \mu\| &= \|\lambda + \chi_K\mu\| + \|(1 - \chi_K)\mu\| \\ &\geq \|\lambda + \chi_K\mu\| + \|\chi_K\mu\| \\ &\geq \|\lambda\| - \|\chi_K\mu\| + \|\chi_K\mu\| = \|\lambda\|,\end{aligned}$$

so T^* is an isometry. But it is easy to see that

T* is an isometry if and only if i) holds. The proof is finished.

We conclude this section with the following remark: *If* K *and* L *are peak sets in the weak sense for the function algebra* A, *so is* $K \cup L$. For whenever $\mu \in A^{\perp}$, $\mu(K \cup L) = \mu(K) + \mu(L) - \mu(K \cap L) = 0$ by Theorem 2.4.7, so $K \cup L$ is a peak set in the weak sense by Theorem 2.4.9. (Note that $\mu(K) = 0$ for all $\mu \in A^{\perp}$ if and only if $\chi_K \mu \in A^{\perp}$ for all $\mu \in A^{\perp}$). This argument is easily modified to show that any closed countable union of peak sets in the weak sense is again a peak set in the weak sense. If K and L are peak sets, Bear has given the following more direct argument that $K \cup L$ is a peak set: let $f \in A$ peak on K, and $g \in A$ peak on L. Since $(1 - z)^{1/2}$ (principal value) is uniformly approximable by polynomials on the closed unit disk, $(1 - f)^{1/2} = h \in A$, and $(1 - g)^{1/2} = k \in A$. Since h vanishes only on K, and k only on L, and since $|\arg h| < \frac{\pi}{4}$ and $|\arg k| < \frac{\pi}{4}$, we have that hk vanishes precisely on $K \cup L$, while $\operatorname{Re} hk > 0$ off $K \cup L$, so e^{-hk} peaks on $K \cup L$.

One can interpret this result as asserting: the peak sets in the weak sense are the closed sets of a topology on X. This topology is evidently weaker than the given topology of X, hence is Hausdorff only if it is identical with the given topology. In view of Theorem 2.4.7, this can occur only when $A = C(X)$.

2-5 REPRESENTING MEASURES AND THE JENSEN INEQUALITY

Consider our standard example, the disk algebra A. The multiplicative linear functional, evaluation at the origin, is represented, as we saw, by normalized Lebesgue measure σ on the circle Γ. This measure σ has additional properties with respect to A:

1) if $f \in A$ is invertible, then

$$\log|f(0)| = \int \log|f|d\sigma,$$

and 2) for any $f \in A$,

$$\log|f(0)| \leq \int \log|f|d\sigma.$$

To see that 1) holds, we just observe that if $f \in A^{-1}$, then $\log f \in A$, and $\log|f(0)| = \text{Re} \log f(0) = \text{Re} \int \log f d\sigma = \int \log|f|d\sigma$. Property 2) is the classical Jensen inequality of function theory. The importance of 1) and 2) in the general setting of function algebras was first appreciated by Arens and Singer [1].

DEFINITION. Let A be a function algebra on X,

$\phi \in \operatorname{Spec} A$, σ a probability measure on X. We say that σ is an *Arens-Singer measure* for ϕ if $\log|\phi(f)| = \int \log|f|d\sigma$ for all $f \in A^{-1}$. We say that σ is a *Jensen measure* for ϕ if

$$\log|\phi(f)| \leq \int \log|f|d\sigma \quad \text{for all } f \in A.$$

We remark that any Jensen measure is necessarily also an Arens-Singer measure. For if σ a Jensen measure, and $f \in A^{-1}$, we have

$$\log|\phi(f)| \leq \int \log|f|d\sigma = - \int \log|f^{-1}|d\sigma$$
$$\leq - \log|\phi(f^{-1})| = \log|\phi(f)|,$$

so equality holds. Also, it is easy to see that an Arens-Singer measure for ϕ is necessarily a representing measure for ϕ. For if $f \in A$, we have

$$\operatorname{Re} \phi(f) = \log|\phi(e^f)| = \int \log|e^f|d\sigma = \int \operatorname{Re} f d\sigma,$$

and similarly, by considering if, $\operatorname{Im} \phi(f) = \int \operatorname{Im} f d\sigma$, so $\phi(f) = \int f d\sigma$.

It can be seen from simple examples that representing measures need not be Arens-Singer measures, and that Arens-Singer measures need not be Jensen measures. For instance, let $0 < r < R < \infty$, let $X = \{|s| = r\} \cup \{|s| = R\}$, and let A be the function algebra on X generated by z and $\frac{1}{z}$, or what is evidently the same, the restriction to X of all functions continuous in the closed annulus $\{r \leq |s| \leq R\}$ and holomorphic in the interior. It is easy to see that every real continuous function on X can be uniformly approximated by functions of the form Re f + c log|z|, with f $\in$ A and c real. This implies that each point in the annulus admits a unique Arens-Singer measure. If σ_1, σ_2 are the normalized Lebesgue measure on the inner and outer boundaries, respectively, it is easy to check that $\sigma_1 - \sigma_2 \in A^\perp$. If $r < |s| < R$, it can be shown that the Arens-Singer measure μ for s is of the form $\mu = p\sigma_1 + q\sigma_2$, where p and q are positive functions bounded away from 0. It follows that $\mu + \varepsilon(\sigma_1 - \sigma_2)$ is a positive measure for ε small enough, hence a representing measure for s which differs from μ and so is not an Arens-Singer measure.

In the next chapter, we will see an example where the only Arens-Singer measures are point masses, while many points admit representing measures other than the point mass.

For an example, where Arens-Singer measures

need not be Jensen measures, again take X to be the union of two circles, this time taking $\Gamma_1 = \{(s, 0) \in \mathbb{C}^2 : |s| = 1\}$ and $\Gamma_2 = \{(0, s) \in \mathbb{C}^2 : |s| = 1\}$, $X = \Gamma_1 \cup \Gamma_2$, and $A = P(X)$, the algebra generated by the coordinate functions z_1 and z_2. There is no difficulty in identifying the maximal ideal space of A with $\{(s, t) \in \mathbb{C}^2 : |s| \leq 1, |t| \leq 1, st = 0\}$, two disks with their centers identified. Let σ_j be normalized Lebesgue measure on Γ_j, $j = 1, 2$. Since either σ_1 or σ_2 is a Jensen measure for (0, 0) (the classical fact), we see that $\sigma_1 - \sigma_2$ annihilates $\log|f|$ for any $f \in A^{-1}$. Now consider evaluation at (s, 0), where $0 < |s| < 1$. The Poisson measure on Γ_1, $\mu = \dfrac{1 - |s|^2}{|1 - s\bar{z}_1|^2}\,\sigma_1$,

is evidently a Jensen measure for (s, 0); it is also the only representing measure for (s, 0) which is supported on Γ_1 (this is a restatement of the fact that representing measures for the disk algebra are unique.) Now for ε sufficiently small, $\mu + \varepsilon(\sigma_2 - \sigma_1)$ is a positive measure, hence an Arens-Singer measure for (s, 0). But any Jensen measure ν for (s, 0) must be supported on Γ_1, since $-\infty < \log|s| \leq \int \log|z_1|\,d\nu$, and $\log|z_1| = -\infty$ on

Γ_2. Thus μ is the unique Jensen measure for (s, 0).

The following basic existence theorem is due to Bishop [5].

THEOREM 2.5.1. *Let* A *be a function algebra on* X, ϕ *a multiplicative linear functional on* A. *Then there exists a Jensen measure for* ϕ.

Proof. Let $P = \{u \in C_R(X)$: there exists $f \in A$ with $\phi(f) = 1$, and a positive integer n, such that $nu > \log|f|\}$, and let $N = \{u \in C_R(X): u < 0\}$. We observe that if u and v belong to P, so does u + v. For if $nu > \log|f|$ and $mv > \log|g|$, where $\phi(f) = \phi(g) = 1$, then $mn(u + v) > m \log|f| + n \log|g| = \log|f^m g^n|$, and $\phi(f^m g^n) = 1$. Also, if r is a positive real number and $u \in P$, then $ru \in P$. For we may assume r is rational, say $r = p/q$, where p and q are positive integers; then if $nu > \log|f|$, $(qn)(ru) > \log|f^p|$. Thus P is a convex cone in $C_R(X)$. Now P is disjoint from the convex cone N, for if $u < 0$ and $nu > \log|f|$, then $\log|f| < 0$, so $|f| < 1$, and hence $|\phi(f)| < 1$. Since P and N are open, by the separation theorem there exists a continuous linear functional on $C_R(X)$ separating P and N, i.e., a real measure σ on X such that

$\int v\,d\sigma \leq \int u\,d\sigma$ for any $v \in N$, $u \in P$. Evidently, σ is a positive measure, which may be chosen to be a probability measure, and $\int u\,d\sigma \geq 0$ whenever $u \in P$. Now if $f \in A$ and $\phi(f) \neq 0$, we have $\int u\,d\sigma \geq 0$ for all $u \in C_R(X)$ with $u > \log \left|\frac{f}{\phi(f)}\right|$, so $\int \log \left|\frac{f}{\phi(f)}\right| d\sigma \geq 0$, i.e., $\log|\phi(f)| \leq \int \log|f|\,d\sigma$. But if $\phi(f) = 0$, this inequality is automatic. Thus σ is a Jensen measure, and the theorem is proved.

One way in which Jensen measures are often employed is to show that certain functions can't vanish too often. Let us illustrate with some classical facts. Let A be the disk algebra on the unit circle. It is easy to see that no $f \in A$, $f \neq 0$, can vanish on a non-empty open subset of the circle, for then a finite number of translates would have their zero sets covering the circle; their product would vanish identically, so some translate would have uncountably many zeroes in the interior, thus $f = 0$. It is less obvious that no $f \in A$, other than 0, can vanish on a subset of Γ having positive measure. The simplest proof is via the Jensen inequality. If $f \neq 0$, we can write $f = z^k g$ for some $k \geq 0$, $g \in A$, $g(0) \neq 0$. Then

$$-\infty < \log|g(0)| \leq \int \log|g|d\sigma = \int \log|f|d\sigma,$$

so $f \neq 0$ a.e. (σ).

We next give a classical theorem of Rado. The proof which follows is essentially due to Glicksberg [2], with the trick of using Jensen measures supplied by Bishop.

Let Δ be the closed unit disk, Γ the unit circle, A the disk algebra on Δ.

THEOREM 2.5.2. *Let* $f \in C(\Delta)$, $E = \{x \in \Delta : f(x) = 0\}$. *If* f *is holomorphic on* int $\Delta \backslash E$, *then* $f \in A$.

Proof. Let B be the function algebra on Δ generated by f and A, let X be the Shilov boundary for B. Since every function in B is holomorphic in int $\Delta \backslash E$, and in int E, $X \subset \Gamma \cup \partial E$. We shall show that $X = \Gamma$. Since $\partial E \subset \overline{\Delta \backslash E}$, it suffices to show that for each $x \in \Delta \backslash E$, $|g(x)| \leq \|g\|_\Gamma$ for all $g \in B$. Let $x \in \Delta \backslash E$, let μ be a Jensen measure for x with respect to B, with supp $\mu \subset X$. Since $0 < |f(x)| \leq \exp \int \log|f|d\mu$, and $f = 0$ on E, $\mu(E) = 0$. Thus for all $g \in B$, $g(x) = \int_\Gamma g d\mu$, so $|g(x)| \leq \|g\|_\Gamma$, as we claimed.

Thus $B|\Gamma$ is a function algebra on Γ which contains the disk algebra on Γ, and is clearly not $C(\Gamma)$. By Wermer's maximality theorem, 1.2.4, $B|\Gamma = A|\Gamma$. Thus $f|\Gamma = h|\Gamma$ for some $h \in A$, and since $f - h \in B$ and vanishes on Γ, $f - h = 0$ on Δ, i.e., $f \in A$, concluding the proof.

Theorem 2.5.2 obviously implies: *if* G *is an open set in* $\mathbb{C}$ *(or more generally, a Riemann surface), if* f *is continuous on* G *and holomorphic outside its zero set, then* f *is holomorphic in* G.

We next give a generalization, due to Bishop, of Hadamard's "Three Circles Theorem".

THEOREM 2.5.3. *Let* A *be a function algebra on* X. *Let* E *and* F *be closed subsets of* X *with* $X = E \cup F$. *Then for each* $\phi \in \operatorname{Spec} A$, *there exists a constant* α, $0 \le \alpha \le 1$, *such that for all* $f \in A$: $|\phi(f)| \le \|f\|_E^{\alpha}\ \|f\|_F^{1-\alpha}$.

Proof. Let μ be a Jensen measure for ϕ. Then for any $f \in A$,

$$\log|\phi(f)| \le \int_X \log|f|\,d\mu$$

$$= \int_E \log|f|\,d\mu + \int_{F\setminus E} \log|f|\,d\mu$$

$$\leq \mu(E)\ \sup\{\log(f(x)) : x \in E\}$$
$$+ \mu(F\backslash E)\sup\{\log|f(x)| : x \in F\}$$

and the theorem, with $\alpha = \mu(E)$, follows by exponentiating both sides.

Applications of this result may be found in Bishop [5], and in Creese [1].

It is often useful to observe that Jensen's inequality persists when we pass to L^1 limits.

THEOREM 2.5.4. *Let* A *be a function algebra on* X, μ *a Jensen measure. Let* $H^1(\mu)$ *denote the closure in* $L^1(\mu)$ *of* A. *Then*

$$\log\left|\int f d\mu\right| \leq \int \log|f| d\mu$$

for all $f \in H^1(\mu)$.

<u>Proof</u>. Let $f_n \in A$, $\int |f - f_n| d\mu \to 0$. We may assume $\int f d\mu \neq 0$, else there is nothing to prove. Now for each n,

$$\log\left|\int f_n d\mu\right| \leq \int \log|f_n| d\mu$$

$$= \int \log^+|f_n| d\mu - \int \log^-|f_n| d\mu$$

or $$\log\left|\int f_n d\mu\right| + \int \log^-|f_n| d\mu \leq \int \log^+|f_n| d\mu.$$

Since $|\log^+|f_n| - \log^+|f|| \leq ||f_n| - |f|| \leq |f_n - f|$

we have $\int \log^+|f_n|d\mu \to \int \log^+|f|d\mu$. Clearly, $\log|\int f_n d\mu| \to \log|\int f d\mu|$. Hence

$$\log\left|\int f d\mu\right| + \liminf \int \log^-|f_n|d\mu \leq \int \log^+|f|d\mu.$$

Now we may assume, passing to a subsequence if necessary, that $f_n \to f$ a.e., and hence that $\log^-|f_n| \to \log^-|f|$ a.e. Applying Fatou's lemma, we have $\liminf \int \log^-|f_n|d\mu \geq \int \log^-|f|d\mu$, so $\log|\int f d\mu| \leq \int \log^+|f|d\mu - \int \log^-|f|d\mu = \int \log|f|d\mu$, as was to be proved.

In the classical case, where A is the disk algebra on the circle, σ normalized Lebesgue measure, $H^1(\sigma)$, and the analogous spaces $H^p(\sigma)$ formed by taking the closure of A in $L^p(\sigma)$, are called *Hardy spaces*. We used $H^2(\sigma)$ (in the general context) already in Section 1 of this chapter, and the spaces $H^p(\sigma)$ will play an important role in Chapter 4.

If A is the disk algebra, we can immediately deduce from Theorem 2.5.4 these classical results: *if* $f \in H^1(\sigma)$ *is not the zero function,* $\log|f|$ *is summable* (a theorem of Szegö); hence, *unless* $f = 0$, f *cannot vanish on a set of positive measure* (the "little" F. and M. Riesz theorem). The proof is immediate from Theorem 2.5.4 if $f(0) \neq 0$; in the general case, we apply this result to $\bar{z}^n f$, where n is appropriately chosen.

At this point, we insert some material for readers unfamiliar with L^p spaces for $0 < p < 1$. Let μ be a probability measure. For f a measurable function, $0 < p < \infty$, we write $\|f\|_p = (\int |f|^p d\mu)^{1/p}$, even though $\| \ \|_p$ is not a norm if $p < 1$.

From the inequality $t^p \leq pt + 1 - p$ when $t \geq 0$, $0 < p < 1$ (easily verified by elementary calculus) it follows that $\int u^p d\mu \leq 1$ whenever u is a non-negative measurable function with $\int u d\mu = 1$, and $0 < p < 1$, and hence

$$\int u^p d\mu \leq \left(\int u d\mu \right)^p \tag{1}$$

for any non-negative measurable u, $0 < p < 1$.

If $0 < r < s$, then $r = sp$, where $0 < p < 1$, and it follows from (1) that $\int u^r d\mu = \int (u^s)^p d\mu \leq (\int u^s d\mu)^p$, whence

$$\|u\|_r \leq \|u\|_s \tag{2}$$

for any measurable u, $0 < r < s < \infty$.

From the inequality $\log t \leq t - 1$ whenever $t > 0$, it follows that if u is a non-negative measurable function and $\int u\,d\mu = 1$, then $\int \log u\,d\mu \leq 0$, and hence for any non-negative u such that $\int \log u\,d\mu$ exists in the extended sense,

$$\exp \int \log u\,d\mu \leq \int u\,d\mu,$$

known as the *inequality of the geometric and arithmetic means*. Replacing u by u^p, it follows at once that

$$\exp \int \log u\,d\mu \leq \|u\|_p \tag{3}$$

for any $u \geq 0$ such that $\int \log u\,d\mu$ exists in the extended sense, and any $p > 0$.

If $t > 0$, it is easily verified by elementary calculus that $\frac{t^p - 1}{p}$ decreases to $\log t$ as p decreases to 0. Suppose u is a non-negative measurable function and $\int u^r d\mu < \infty$ for some $r > 0$. Then for $0 < p \leq r$, we have

$$\log\|u\|_p = \frac{1}{p} \log \int u^p d\mu$$
$$\leq \frac{1}{p}\left(\int u^p d\mu - 1\right) = \int \frac{u^p - 1}{p}\, d\mu,$$

so applying the monotone convergence theorem, we get $\inf_{p>0} \|u\|_p \leq \exp \int \log u\,d\mu$. Combining this with (2) and (3), we find that

$$\exp \int \log u\,d\mu = \inf_{p>0} \|u\|_p = \lim_{p\to 0} \|u\|_p \tag{4}$$

whenever u is a non-negative measurable function, and the right-hand side is finite.

The arguments of the last two paragraphs are due to F. Riesz [1].

From the fact that the elementary inequalities which we used are equalities if and only if $t = 1$, it follows that (1), (2), and (3) are equalities if and only if $u = \text{const. a.e. } (\mu)$.

From this characterization of the geometric mean, we have at once:

LEMMA 2.5.5. *Let* A *be a function algebra on* X, μ *a probability measure on* X. *Then* μ *is a Jensen measure* (*for some* $\phi \in \operatorname{Spec} A$) *if and only if*

$$\left| \int f\,d\mu \right|^p \leq \int |f|^p d\mu$$

for all $f \in A$, *all* $p > 0$.

It is obvious that one could also prove Theorem 2.5.4 by using this lemma. Similarly, this lemma implies that μ is a Jensen measure for ϕ whenever $|\phi(f)| \leq \exp \int \log|f|d\mu$ for all f in a dense subset of A.

2-6 REPRESENTING MEASURES AND SCHWARZ'S LEMMA

Let A be the disk algebra on the disk Δ. A very useful classical fact, known as Schwarz's Lemma, asserts that if $f \in A$ and $f(0) = 0$, then $|f(s)| \leq |s| \, \|f\|$ for all $s \in \Delta$ (proof: apply the maximum principle to $\frac{f}{z}$). By composing with linear fractional transformations, we can give this a formulation not distinguishing the point 0: if $|s| < 1$, $|t| < 1$, $f \in A$, $\|f\| < 1$, then $|f(s) - f(t)| \leq \left|\frac{s - t}{1 - \bar{s}t}\right| |1 - \overline{f(s)} f(t)|$. The first factor being strictly less than 1, we see that $\sup\{|f(s) - f(t)|: f \in A, \|f\| \leq 1\} < 2$ whenever $|s| < 1$, $|t| < 1$. On the other hand, if $|s| = 1$, $|t| \leq 1$, this sup = 2: for let $f_r = \bar{s} \dfrac{z - rs}{1 - r\bar{s}z}$, for $0 < r < 1$; then $\|f_r\| = 1$, $f_r(s) = 1$, and $f_r(t) = \dfrac{\bar{s}t - r}{1 - r\bar{s}t} \to -1$ as $r \to 1$. Identifying points of Δ with the corresponding multiplicative linear functionals, we have shown that $\|s - t\| < 2$ if and only if both s and t are interior points of Δ; thus Spec A (A the disk algebra) is divided into equivalence classes by the relation $\|s - t\| < 2$. In 1956, Gleason [1] made the remarkable discovery that this holds true for any function algebra, and proposed that the search for analytic structure in the maximal ideal space should proceed via the investigation of the metric topology. This idea has proved successful in the context of Dirichlet algebras (defined by Gleason in the same paper) and their generalizations, as we shall see in Chapter 4.

Till further notice, A will be a function algebra on X.

LEMMA 2.6.1. *Let* ϕ, $\psi \in$ Spec A. *Then* $\|\phi - \psi\| < 2$ *if and only if*

$$\sup\{|\psi(f)|: f \in A, \|f\| \leq 1, \phi(f) = 0\} < 1.$$

Proof. Suppose $\|\phi - \psi\| = 2c < 2$. Let $f \in A$, $\|f\| \leq 1$, $\phi(f) = 0$; we can assume that $\psi(f) > 0$. Put $g = \dfrac{c - f}{1 - cf}$; then $g \in A$, $\|g\| \leq 1$, so $|\phi(g) - \psi(g)| \leq 2c$, i.e., $\left|c - \dfrac{c - \psi(f)}{1 - c\psi(f)}\right| \leq 2c$, from which we find $(1 - c^2)\psi(f) \leq 2c(1 - c\psi(f))$, whence $\psi(f) \leq \dfrac{2c}{1 + c^2} < 1$.

Now suppose $|\psi(f)| \leq c < 1$ whenever $f \in A$, $\|f\| \leq 1$, $\phi(f) = 0$. If $g \in A$ and $\|g\| < 1$, put $f = \dfrac{g - \phi(g)}{1 - \overline{\phi(g)}g}$. Then $f \in A$, $\|f\| < 1$, and $\phi(f) = 0$, so $|\psi(f)| \leq c$, i.e.,

$$|\psi(g) - \phi(g)| \leq c|1 - \overline{\phi(g)}\psi(g)| \leq 2c,$$

so $\|\phi - \psi\| < 2$. The lemma is proved.

The next characterization is entirely similar.

LEMMA 2.6.2. *Let* $\phi, \psi \in$ Spec A, $0 < c < 1$. *If there exists a sequence* $\{f_n\}$ *in* A, $\|f_n\| < 1$, *with* $|\phi(f_n)| \leq c$ *all* n, *and* $|\psi(f_n)| \to 1$, *then* $\|\phi - \psi\| = 2$.

Proof. Passing to a subsequence, we may assume $\phi(f_n) \to a$, $|a| < 1$, and $\psi(f_n) \to b$, $|b| = 1$. Let $g_n = \dfrac{f_n - \phi(f_n)}{1 - \overline{\phi(f_n)}f_n}$; then $g_n \in A$, $\|g_n\| < 1$, $\phi(g_n) = 0$, and $|\psi(g_n)| \to \left|\dfrac{b - a}{1 - \bar{a}b}\right| = 1$, so $\|\phi - \psi\| = 2$ by Lemma 2.6.1.

THEOREM 2.6.3. *For* $\phi, \psi \in$ Spec A, *write* $\phi \sim \psi$ *if and only if* $\|\phi - \psi\| < 2$. *Then* $\sim$ *is an equivalence relation on* Spec A.

Proof. Reflexivity and symmetry are obvious. Suppose $\theta \sim \phi$ and $\phi \sim \psi$. If $\theta \not\sim \psi$, by Lemma 2.6.1 there exist $f_n \in A$, $\|f_n\| < 1$, $\theta(f_n) = 0$, $|\psi(f_n)| \to 1$. By the same lemma, there exists $c < 1$ such that $|\phi(f_n)| \leq c$, since $\theta \sim \phi$. But since $\phi \sim \psi$, this contradicts Lemma 2.6.2. Hence $\theta \sim \psi$, and the theorem is proved.

DEFINITION. The *Gleason parts*, or simply *parts*,

are the equivalence classes defined by the relation $\sim$.

If a subset M of Spec A can be given the structure of connected complex manifold in such a way that the functions in A are holomorphic on M, then M is contained in a single Gleason part. For any two points of M can be connected by a finite chain of analytic disks, and the classical Schwarz lemma and Lemma 2.6.1 applied repeatedly. However, parts can be large without the presence of any analytic structure, as we shall see in the next chapter. Indeed, unless some restrictive assumptions are imposed, essentially nothing can be said about the structure of parts in general. For instance, it was conjectured that parts might have to be connected, or at least could not be finite sets, other than singletons. But Garnett [1] proved the following striking result: *given any completely regular, σ-compact space* P, *there exists a function algebra in whose maximal ideal space* P *can be imbedded as a single Gleason part; further, every bounded continuous function on* P *is the restriction of some function in the algebra.* (It is clear that parts must be completely regular, as subsets of a compact Hausdorff space, and σ-compact, since for any $\phi \in \text{Spec } A$, $\{\psi \in \text{Spec } A\colon \|\phi - \psi\| \leq 2 - \frac{1}{n}\}$ is compact by the Banach-Alaoglu theorem.) A conjecture of long standing was that if every part of A reduces to a single point, then $A = C(X)$. This conjecture fell, of course, with the peak point conjecture, since peak points are obviously one-point parts.

We now turn our attention to what can be said about representing measures in relation to parts. We first observe that if $\|\phi - \psi\| = 2$, and λ, μ are representing measures for ϕ, ψ respectively, then λ and μ must be mutually singular (for $\lambda - \mu$ represents $\phi - \psi$, so $\|\lambda - \mu\| \geq 2$, and since λ and μ are probability measures, it easily follows that they are singular.) We can formulate this remark as: *a sufficient condition that ϕ and ψ lie in the same Gleason part is that they admit representing measures which are not singular*. The converse, and even more, turns out to be true. The next theorem was first obtained by Gleason in the context of Dirichlet algebras; the general result is due to Bishop ([6] and [7]). We shall follow Bishop's second proof, which yields a good deal more than is stated in the theorem.

THEOREM 2.6.4. *Let* A *be a function algebra on* X, ϕ, $\psi \in$ Spec A, $\|\phi - \psi\| < 2$. *Then there exist constants* a *and* b, $0 < a \leq b < \infty$, *a Borel function* h *on* X *with* $a \leq h \leq b$, *and representing measures* λ *and* μ *for* ϕ *and* ψ *respectively, such that* $\mu = h\lambda$.

Proof. Let $M = \{f \in A: \phi(f) = 0\}$, the maximal ideal associated with ϕ. Let ψ' be the restriction of ψ to M. By Lemma 2.6.1, $\|\psi'\| = c < 1$. Hence there exists a (complex) measure ν on X with $\|\nu\| = c$ and $\psi(f) = \int f d\nu$ for all $f \in M$. Let $f_n \in M$, $\|f_n\| \leq 1$, with $\psi(f_n) \to c$. We regard the f_n as points in $L^\infty(|\nu|) = L^1(|\nu|)^*$. Since the closed unit ball of a dual space is weak* compact, $\{f_n\}$ has a weak* cluster point $Z \in L^\infty(|\nu|)$, $|Z| \leq 1$. We have then

$$c = \liminf \left| \int f_n d\nu \right| \leq \left| \int Z d\nu \right|$$

$$\leq \int |Z| d|\nu| \leq c,$$

from which follows that $|Z| = 1$, and in fact that $\overline{Z} = \frac{d\nu}{d|\nu|}$; thus $\{f_n\}$ actually converges to Z (weak-*). Let $\mu = \frac{1}{c}|\nu| = \frac{1}{c} Z\nu$. Then μ is a probability measure on X, and for any $g \in A$, we have (using the fact that $gf_n \in M$, all n):

$$c\int g\,d\mu = \int gZ\,d\nu = \lim \int gf_n\,d\nu = \lim \psi(gf_n)$$
$$= \lim \psi(g)\psi(f_n) = c\psi(g).$$

Thus μ is a representing measure for ψ. Now for any $g \in M$, $\psi(g) = \int g\,d\mu = \int g\,d\nu = \int gc\bar{Z}\,d\mu$, so $\int g(1 - c\bar{Z})d\mu = 0$. In particular, $\int f_n(1 - c\bar{Z})d\mu = 0$ for all n, hence $\int Z(1 - c\bar{Z})d\mu = 0$, so $\int Z\,d\mu = c$, and hence $\int (1 - cZ)(1 - c\bar{Z})d\mu = 1 - c^2$. Also, for $g \in M$, $g(1 - cf_n) \in M$, so $\int g(1 - cf_n)(1 - c\bar{Z})d\mu = 0$, and hence $\int g|1 - cZ|^2 d\mu = 0$. Let $\lambda = \frac{|1 - cZ|^2}{1 - c^2}\mu$; then λ is a probability measure which annihilates M, hence a representing measure for ϕ. We have $\mu = \frac{1 - c^2}{|1 - cZ|^2}\lambda$, and the theorem is proved, with $a = \frac{1 - c^2}{(1 + c)^2} = \frac{1 - c}{1 + c}$, and $b = \frac{1 + c}{1 - c}$.

A few remarks are in order concerning this theorem, and its proof. One observes that we have a formal similarity to the classical Poisson formula, from which follows a version of Harnack's inequality in the abstract setting: if $f \in A$, and $\operatorname{Re} f \geq 0$ on X, we have

$$\frac{1 - c}{1 + c} \operatorname{Re} \phi(f) \leq \operatorname{Re} \psi(f) \leq \frac{1 + c}{1 - c} \operatorname{Re} \phi(f).$$

Another point to notice is this: let $H^2_\phi(\mu)$ be the closure of M in $L^2(\mu)$. Then cZ is the projection of 1 on $H^2_\phi(\mu)$; for clearly $cZ \in H^2_\phi(\mu)$, and since $\int g(1 - c\overline{Z})d\mu = 0$ for all $g \in M$, this relation holds for all $g \in H^2_\phi(\mu)$, i.e., $1 - cZ \perp H^2_\phi$. The linear functional ψ' on M extends to a continuous linear functional on H^2_ϕ (in fact $\psi(g) = (g, cZ)$ as we saw, where (,) is the L^2 inner product). The norm of the extended functional is clearly c. Thus we have the perhaps surprising equality:

$$\sup\{|\psi(g)| : g \in M, \|g\| \leq 1\}$$
$$= \sup\{|\psi(g)| : g \in M, \int |g|^2 d\mu \leq 1\}.$$

Harnack"s inequality can be deduced more directly. Suppose ϕ and ψ belong to the same Gleason part, so there exists a constant $c < 1$ such that $|\psi(g)| < c$ whenever $g \in A$, $\|g\| < 1$, and $\phi(g) = 0$. Now if $f \in A$ and $\operatorname{Re} f > 0$, put $g = (1 - f) \times (1 + f)^{-1}$; then $g \in A$, $\|g\| < 1$. If $\phi(f) = 1$, then $\phi(g) = 0$, so $|\psi(g)| < c$, or $|1 - \psi(f)| < c|1 + \psi(f)|$, whence, by a simple computation, $\operatorname{Re} \psi(f) < (1 + c) \times (1 - c)^{-1}$. It follows that $\operatorname{Re} \psi(f) < (1 + c)(1 - c)^{-1} \operatorname{Re} \phi(f)$ whenever $\operatorname{Re} f > 0$.

It is interesting to note that the existence of boundedly mutually absolutely continuous representing measures can be deduced from Harnack's inequality, and thus can be regarded as a theorem about linear subspaces of $C(X)$, rather than function algebras. The next theorem is due to Bishop [6], and evidently contains Theorem 2.6.4.

THEOREM 2.6.5. *Let* B *be a linear subspace of* $C_R(X)$, *containing the constant functions. Let* ϕ, $\psi \in B^*$, *with* $\|\phi\| = \phi(1) = \|\psi\| = \psi(1) = 1$. *Suppose there exists* k *such that* $\phi(u) < k\psi(u)$ *and* $\psi(u) < k\phi(u)$ *whenever* $u \in B$ *and* $u > 0$. *Then there exist representing measures* λ *for* ϕ *and* μ *for* ψ *with* $\lambda \leq k\mu$ *and* $\mu \leq k\lambda$.

Proof. Let $\theta = k\psi - \phi$. We show that there exists a positive measure σ representing θ. To this end, put $P = \{u \in B : \theta(u) \geq 0\}$ and $N = \{u \in C_R(X) : u < 0\}$. If $u \in B$ and $u < 0$, then $\theta(u) < 0$ by hypothesis, so P and N are disjoint. Clearly, P and N are convex cones, and N is open. Applying the separation theorem, we find a measure σ on X such that $\int v d\sigma \leq \int u d\sigma$ whenever $v \in N$ and $u \in P$. It is obvious that $\sup\{\int v d\sigma : v \in N\}$ must be 0, so σ is a positive measure, and $\int u d\sigma \geq 0$ for all $u \in P$;

we may assume that $\int d\sigma = k - 1$. Now if $u \in B$, we have $\pm (u - (k - 1)^{-1}\theta(u)) \in P$, so $\int u d\sigma = \theta(u)$.

Interchanging the roles of ϕ and ψ, we find similarly a positive measure τ on X such that $\int u d\tau = k\phi(u) - \psi(u)$ for all $u \in B$. Put $\lambda = (k^2 - 1)^{-1}(k\tau + \sigma)$ and $\mu = (k^2 - 1)^{-1}(k\sigma + \tau)$. Then for any $u \in B$,

$$\int u d\lambda = (k^2 - 1)^{-1}[k^2\phi(u) - k\psi(u) + k\psi(u) - \phi(u)] = \phi(u),$$

and similarly, $\int u d\mu = \psi(u)$. Clearly $0 \leq \lambda \leq k\mu$ and $\mu \leq k\lambda$. The theorem is proved.

2-7 ANTISYMMETRIC ALGEBRAS

If the real functions in a function algebra A on X separate the points of X, the Stone-Weierstrass theorem tells us that $A = C(X)$. In this section, we obtain a useful refinement of this result.

DEFINITION. Let A be a function algebra on X. We say that A is *antisymmetric* if every real function in A is constant. A subset E of X is called a *set of antisymmetry* (for A) if $f \in A$ and $f|E$ real implies $f|E$ is constant.

Evidently, $\{x\}$ is a set of antisymmetry for

each $x \in X$; A is antisymmetric if and only if X is a set of antisymmetry. If μ is a representing measure for some $\phi \in \text{Spec } A$, then supp μ is a set of antisymmetry: for if $f \in A$, and f is real on supp μ, then equality holds in the Schwarz inequality, since $\int f^2 d\mu = (\int f d\mu)^2$, hence f = const. a.e. (μ), and hence f is constant on supp μ.

LEMMA 2.7.1. *If* E *and* F *are sets of antisymmetry, and* $E \cap F$ *is not empty, then* $E \cup F$ *is a set of antisymmetry. Hence, if* E *and* F *are maximal sets of antisymmetry, either* E = F *or* E *and* F *are disjoint.*

Proof. Obvious.

LEMMA 2.7.2. *Every set of antisymmetry is contained in a maximal set of antisymmetry.*

Proof. If $\{E_\alpha\}$ is a collection of sets of antisymmetry, linearly ordered by inclusion, it is clear that $\cup E_\alpha$ is a set of antisymmetry. The lemma now follows by Zorn's lemma.

It is clear that the closure of a set of antisymmetry is again a set of antisymmetry, hence maximal sets of antisymmetry must be closed. More is true:

LEMMA 2.7.3. *Let* E *be a maximal set of antisymmetry.*

Then E *is a peak set in the weak sense.*

Proof. Let F be the intersection of all peak sets which contain E; then $E \subset F$, and F is a peak set in the weak sense. If $E \neq F$, then (since E is a maximal set of antisymmetry) there exists $f \in A$, with $f|F$ real and not constant. But $f|E$ is constant, say $f = c$ on E. Put $g = 1 - \varepsilon(f - c)^2$, where $0 < \varepsilon < \frac{1}{4}\|f\|^{-2}$. Then $g|F$ peaks on a proper subset K of F, $K \supset E$. By Corollary 2.4.4, K is a peak set for A, contradicting the definition of F. Thus $E = F$, and the lemma is proved.

The following lemma, due to de Branges [1], is the crucial ingredient for the proof of our central result.

LEMMA 2.7.4. *Let* μ *be an extreme point of the closed unit ball of* $A^{\perp}$. *Then* supp μ *is a set of antisymmetry.*

Proof. Suppose $f \in A$ is real-valued on supp μ. We must show f is constant on supp μ. Replacing f, if necessary, by $af + b$ (a, b real constants) we may assume that $0 < f < 1$ on supp μ. Since $f \in A$ and

A is an algebra, $f\mu \in A^{\perp}$. Now $\mu = \|f\mu\| \dfrac{f\mu}{\|f\mu\|} + \|(1 - f)\mu\| \dfrac{(1 - f)\mu}{\|(1 - f)\mu\|}$, and $\|f\mu\| + \|(1 - f)\mu\| = \int f d|\mu| + \int (1 - f)d|\mu| = 1$, since f and 1 - f are positive. Since μ is an extreme point of the unit ball of $A^{\perp}$, it follows that $\mu = \dfrac{f\mu}{\|f\mu\|}$, so $f = \|f\mu\|$ a.e. (μ), and since f is continuous, f is constant on supp μ. The lemma is proved.

We have now assembled all that is needed for the following proof (due to Glicksberg [1]) of a theorem due to Bishop [3].

THEOREM 2.7.5. *Let* A *be a function algebra on* X. *Let* $\{X_\alpha\}$ *be the collection of distinct maximal sets of antisymmetry for* A. *Then*

i) $X = \cup X_\alpha$, *and the* X_α *are pairwise disjoint;*

ii) $A|X_\alpha$ *is uniformly closed, and antisymmetric;*

iii) $A = \{f \in C(X) : f|X_\alpha \in A|X_\alpha$ *for every* $\alpha\}$.

Proof. i) follows from Lemmas 2.7.1 and 2.7.2, and the observation that singletons are sets of antisymmetry. ii) follows from Lemma 2.7.3, Corollary 2.4.3, and the definition of sets of antisymmetry.

Suppose $f \in C(X)$ and $f|X_\alpha \in A|X_\alpha$ for every α. Then for every extreme point μ in the closed unit ball of $A^\perp$, $f|\text{supp } \mu \in A|\text{supp } \mu$, by Lemmas 2.7.4 and 2.7.2, hence $\int f d\mu = 0$. By the Krein-Milman theorem, it follows that $\int f d\mu = 0$ for all $\mu \in A^\perp$, hence $f \in A$. The proof is finished.

We observe that Theorem 2.7.5 contains the Stone-Weierstrass theorem, since if the real functions in A separate points, no set of antisymmetry can contain more than one point. This is de Branges' proof of the Stone-Weierstrass theorem.

Often, where Theorem 2.7.5 can be applied, a coarser and more obvious decomposition of X serves as well. For each $x \in X$, let $E_x = \{y \in X : f(y) = f(x)$ for all real $f \in A\}$. Since for each real $f \in A$, $\{y \in X : f(y) = f(x)\}$ is a peak set (as we saw above, $1 - \varepsilon(f - f(x))^2$ peaks there, for $\varepsilon > 0$ small enough), each E_x is a peak set in the weak sense. It is clear that for $x, y \in A$, either $E_x = E_y$ or E_x and E_y are disjoint. If $f \in A$ is real on X, then f is constant on each E_x, but $A|E_x$ need not be antisymmetric. If $f \in C(X)$, and $f|E_x \in A|E_x$ for each E_x, then $f \in A$: this follows from Lemma 2.7.4, or can be proved directly. The partitioning of X in this fashion was introduced by Shilov, and is the basis for Bishop's proof of Theorem 2.7.5.

Theorem 2.7.5 was used by Hoffman and Wermer [1] to obtain the following theorem.

THEOREM 2.7.6. *Let* A *be a function algebra on* X, *and suppose* Re A *is uniformly closed. Then* A = C(X).

<u>Proof</u>. We shall give first an argument found by the author [1] which does not use Theorem 2.7.5, but which depends on an interesting lemma from functional analysis, found by H. Reiter [1]. If S is a subset of a Banach space B, $S^{\perp}$ denotes $\{\lambda \in B^*: \lambda(f) = 0$ for every $f \in S\}$.

LEMMA 2.7.7. *Let* B *be a Banach space,* S *and* T *closed subspaces of* B. *Then* S + T *is closed if and only if* $S^{\perp} + T^{\perp}$ *is (norm) closed, if and only if* $S^{\perp} + T^{\perp}$ *is weak*-closed.*

<u>Proof</u>. Let i be the inclusion map of S into B, and π the canonical projection of B onto B/T. Then S + T is closed if and only if $\pi \circ i: S \to B/T$ has closed

range. But $\pi \circ i$ has closed range if and only if $(\pi \circ i)^* : (B/T)^* \to S^*$ has closed range. Now $(B/T)^*$ is canonically identified with $T^\perp$, and S^* with $B^*/S^\perp$; the inclusion i' of $T^\perp$ into B^* is (with this identification) the adjoint of π, and the projection $\pi' : B^* \to B^*/S^\perp$ is the adjoint of i. Thus $\pi \circ i$ has closed range if and only if $\pi' \circ i'$: $T^\perp \to B^*/S^\perp$ has closed range, i.e., if and only if $S^\perp + T^\perp$ is closed. The range of an adjoint map is closed if and only if it is weak=* closed. The lemma is proved.

We return to the proof of Theorem 2.7.6. To say Re A is closed is evidently equivalent to saying $A + \overline{A}$ is closed, which by Lemma 2.7.7 implies that $A^\perp + \overline{A}^\perp$ is weak-* closed, i.e., that $(A \cap \overline{A})^\perp = A^\perp + \overline{A}^\perp = A^\perp + \overline{A^\perp}$. For each $x \in X$, let $E_x = \{y \in X : f(y) = f(x)$ for all real $f \in A\}$. We shall show that each $E_x = \{x\}$. Suppose E_x contains more than one point. We have seen that E_x is a peak set in the weak sense, hence there exists a peak set K for A whose intersection with E_x is a non-empty proper subset of E_x (see 2.4.5). Let $p \in E_x \cap K$, $q \in E_x \backslash K$. Then $\delta_p - \delta_q$ annihilates every real $f \in A$, hence $\delta_p - \delta_q \perp A \cap \bar{A}$. From the first sentence of the proof, this implies there exists a real measure ν such that $\delta_p - \delta_q + i\nu = \mu \in A^{\perp}$. If f peaks on K, we have $\int f^n d\mu = 0$ all n, but $f^n \to \chi_K$ boundedly, whence $1 + i\nu(K) = 0$. This is impossible, since ν is real, and thus $E_x = \{x\}$, and the theorem follows from the Stone-Weierstrass theorem.

The original proof of Theorem 2.7.6 went as follows. Suppose first that A is antisymmetric. We show that X reduces to a singleton. Fix $x \in X$, and put $A_x = \{f \in A : f(x) = 0\}$; we regard A_x as a Banach space over the reals. Since A is antisymmetric, the map $f \to \text{Im } f$ is a one-one, norm-decreasing linear map of A_x onto Re A_x. If Re A is closed, so is Re A_x, so the open mapping theorem applies, and assures us that there exists a constant k such that $\|f\| \le k\|\text{Im } f\|$ for all $f \in A_x$. Now if $X \neq \{x\}$, there exists $g \in A_x$ with $\|g\| = 1$; we may assume $g(y) = 1$ for some $y \in X$. Choose r with $1 - e^{-2k} < r < 1$. Put $f = \log(1 - rg)$, where we take the principal value of log. Since log can be uniformly approximated by polynomials on

$\{s: |s - 1| \le r\}$, we have $f \in A$. Clearly, $f(x) = 0$, $|\text{Im } f| < \frac{\pi}{2}$, and $f(y) = \log(1 - r) < -2k$. Thus $\|f\| > k\|\text{Im } f\|$. This contradiction shows that $X = \{x\}$.

For the general case, one shows that if Re A is closed, and Y is a maximal set of antisymmetry for A, then Re $A|Y$ is closed (see Hoffman and Wermer [1] for the details). Applying the argument above, we find that each maximal set of antisymmetry reduces to a single point, and hence $A = C(X)$.

A companion theorem to Theorem 2.7.6 was found by Wermer: *if* Re A *is a ring* (*i.e., if* $u \in$ Re A *implies* $u^2 \in$ Re A), *then* $A = C(X)$. In this case, the reduction to the antisymmetric case is obvious. The proof again is based on the unboundedness of the map Re f → Im f of Re A_x onto itself. The reference is Wermer [4].

A generalization of Theorem 2.7.6 was found by Sidney and Stout [1]: *if* K *is a closed subset of* X, *and* Re $A|K$ *is closed, then* $A|K = C(K)$.

2-8 THE ESSENTIAL SET.

One rather trivial way of making new function

algebras out of old ones runs as follows: if A is a function algebra on X, imbed X in the space Y, and let $B = \{f \in C(Y) : f|X \in A\}$. For example, if A is the disk algebra on the disk Δ, and we take $X = \Delta \times [0, 1]$, and $B = \{f \in C(X) : f(\cdot, 0) \in A\}$, we have a so-called "tomato can" algebra. This particular algebra provides an example of analytic structure in the Shilov boundary, but somehow not a satisfying example. In this brief section, we systemize the discounting of such constructions.

DEFINITION: We say that the function algebra A on X is *essential* if there exists no proper closed subset Y of X such that A contains every continuous function on X which vanishes on Y.

(This notion is due to H. S. Bear.)

We next show that the study of function algebras can be reduced to the study of essential function algebras. (In a sense, this was already done in the last section, since obviously antisymmetric algebras must be essential.)

THEOREM 2.8.1. *Let* A *be a function algebra on* X. *Then there exists a unique minimal closed subset*

E *of* X, *called the* essential set *for* A, *with the property that* A *contains every continuous function on* X *which vanishes on* E. *Further,* E *is a peak set in the weak sense, so* $A|E$ *is closed, and* $A = \{f \in C(X) : f|E \in A|E\}$.

Proof. Let $\mathcal{F}$ be the family of all closed subsets F of X with the property: $A \supset \{f \in C(X) : f|F = 0\}$. Let $E = \cap \{F : F \in \mathcal{F}\}$. To establish the theorem, we must show $E \in \mathcal{F}$. Suppose $f \in C(X)$ vanishes on E. If U is any neighborhood of E, there exists (by the finite intersection principle) $F \in \mathcal{F}$ such that $E \subset F \subset U$. Since $F \in \mathcal{F}$, there exists (Urysohn's Lemma) $g \in A$, such that $g = 0$ on F, $g = 1$ on $X \backslash U$, and $0 \leq g \leq 1$ on X. Then $fg \in A$, since $F \in \mathcal{F}$, and $|fg - f| \leq |f|$ on U, while $fg - f$ vanishes on $X \backslash U$. Choosing $U = \{x : |f(x)| < \varepsilon\}$, we have $\|fg - f\| < \varepsilon$, and $fg \in A$. Hence $f \in A$. Thus $E \in \mathcal{F}$. The remaining assertions are trivial.

An alternate proof explains the essential set in terms of annihilating measures. Let E be the closure of the union of the supports of all annihilating measures for A. I.e., $x \in X \backslash E$ if and only if there exists a neighborhood U of x such that $|\mu|(U) = 0$ for every $\mu \perp A$. Then if $f \in C(X)$ and $f|E \in A|E$, we have $\int f d\mu = 0$ for every $\mu \perp A$, so $f \in A$. On the other hand, if $F \not\supset E$, there exists $\mu \perp A$ such that $|\mu|(X\backslash F) > 0$, and hence there exists $f \in C(X)$, vanishing outside a compact subset of $X\backslash F$, such that $\int f d\mu \neq 0$. Thus A does not contain every $f \in C(X)$ which vanishes on F: E is minimal, and unique.

Evidently, E is empty if and only if $A = C(X)$, and $E = X$ if and only if A is essential. While antisymmetric algebras are essential, essential algebras need not be antisymmetric. The simplest example is $P(X)$, where X is the union of two disjoint closed disks. A connected example is the tomato can algebra: $X = \Delta \times [0, 1]$, A the disk algebra on Δ, $B = \{f \in C(X) : f(\cdot, t) \in A \text{ for all } t \in [0, 1]\}$. Here B is an essential algebra on X, but the maximal sets of antisymmetry are the disks $\Delta \times \{t\}$. In general, the points of $X\backslash E$ are maximal sets of antisymmetry, and any closed subset of $X\backslash E$ is a peak set in the weak sense, as is E.

CHAPTER THREE

RATIONAL APPROXIMATION

3-1 PRELIMINARIES

This chapter is devoted to analysis in the complex plane $\mathbb{C}$, with occasional reference to the Riemann sphere $\hat{\mathbb{C}}$. We continue to reserve the symbol z for the identity function on $\mathbb{C}$. If U is an open set in $\mathbb{C}$, we denote by $C^{(k)}(U)$ the set of all complex-valued functions on U having continuous partial derivatives up to order k; $C_c^{(k)}(U) = \{f \in C^{(k)}(U)\colon f \text{ has compact support in } U\}$. We abbreviate $C_c^{(k)}(\mathbb{C})$ by $C_c^{(k)}$. The first order partial differential operators $\frac{\partial}{\partial z}$, $\frac{\partial}{\partial \bar{z}}$ are defined by

$$\frac{\partial f}{\partial z} = \frac{1}{2}\left(\frac{\partial f}{\partial x} - i\,\frac{\partial f}{\partial y}\right), \quad \frac{\partial}{\partial \bar{z}} = \frac{1}{2}\left(\frac{\partial f}{\partial x} + i\,\frac{\partial f}{\partial y}\right),$$

where we temporarily denote the real coordinates

on $\mathbb{C}$ by x and y, so $z = x + iy$. (We shall never use real coordinates again, and x and y will be available to denote points in $\mathbb{C}$.) The operators $\frac{\partial}{\partial z}$, $\frac{\partial}{\partial \bar{z}}$ are dual to the complex diferentials $dz = dx + idy$, $d\bar{z} = dx - idy$, so $df = \frac{\partial f}{\partial z} dz + \frac{\partial f}{\partial \bar{z}} d\bar{z}$ for any $f \in C^{(1)}(U)$. A necessary and sufficient condition that f be holomorphic in U is that $f \in C^{(1)}(U)$ and $\partial f/\partial \bar{z} = 0$ in U (Cauchy-Riemann equations). We often denote $\frac{\partial f}{\partial z}$ by f_z, $\frac{\partial f}{\partial \bar{z}}$ by $f_{\bar{z}}$. Lebesgue two-dimensional measure in $\mathbb{C}$ will be denoted by m. We write $\Delta(a; r) = \{s \in \mathbb{C} : |s - a| < r\}$.

LEMMA 3.1.1. *Let* K *be a measurable plane set. Then for all* $\zeta \in \mathbb{C}$, $\int_K \frac{dm}{|\zeta - z|} \leq 2\sqrt{\pi m(K)}$. *In particular,* $\frac{1}{z}$ *is summable on compact sets.*

Proof. If $m(K) = \infty$ (or 0) there is nothing to prove. If $m(K) < \infty$, let $R = \sqrt{m(K)/\pi}$, so $m(K) = \pi R^2$. Now put $D = \Delta(\zeta; R)$; then

$$\int_D \frac{dm}{|\zeta - z|} = \int_0^{2\pi} \int_0^R \frac{1}{r} \, r dr d\theta = 2\pi R = 2\sqrt{\pi m(K)},$$

so it remains to show that

$$\int_K \frac{dm}{|\zeta - z|} \le \int_D \frac{dm}{|\zeta - z|}.$$

But $K = [K \cap D] \cup [K\backslash D]$, and $m(K) = m(D)$, so we have $m(K\backslash D) = m(D\backslash K)$. Since $\frac{1}{|\zeta - z|} \ge \frac{1}{R}$ on $D\backslash K$, and $\frac{1}{|\zeta - z|} \le \frac{1}{R}$ on $K\backslash D$, it follows that

$$\int_{K\backslash D} \frac{dm}{|\zeta - z|} \le \int_{D\backslash K} \frac{dm}{|\zeta - z|}, \text{ and hence that}$$

$$\int_K \frac{dm}{|\zeta - z|} = \int_{K\cap D} + \int_{K\backslash D} \le \int_{K\cap D} + \int_{D\backslash K}$$

$$= \int_D \frac{dm}{|\zeta - z|},$$

and the lemma is proved.

The next lemma supplies the main tool in studying rational approximation.

LEMMA 3.1.2. *Let* G *be a bounded plane domain with smooth positively oriented boundary* γ. *Let* $f \in C^{(1)}(U)$, *where* U *is a neighborhood of* $\overline{G}$. *Then for all* $w \in G$,

$$f(w) = \frac{1}{2\pi i} \int_\gamma \frac{f dz}{z - w} - \frac{1}{\pi} \int_G \frac{f_{\bar{z}}}{z - w} dm.$$

Proof. Choose $\varepsilon > 0$ small enough so that $\overline{\Delta(w; \varepsilon)} \subset G$. Let $G_\varepsilon = G\backslash\overline{\Delta(w; \varepsilon)}$. Then G_ε is a smoothly bounded domain with boundary $\gamma - \gamma_\varepsilon$, where γ_ε denotes the circle $\{s: |s - w| = \varepsilon\}$ with positive orientation. By Green's theorem, we have

$$\int_\gamma \frac{f dz}{z - w} - \int_{\gamma_\varepsilon} \frac{f dz}{z - w} = \iint_{G_\varepsilon} \frac{\partial}{\partial \bar{z}} \left(\frac{f}{z - w} \right) d\bar{z} \wedge dz$$

$$= 2i \iint_{G_\varepsilon} \frac{f_{\bar{z}}}{z - w} dm.$$

Now $\displaystyle\int_{\gamma_\varepsilon} \frac{f dz}{z - w} = i \int_0^{2\pi} f(w + \varepsilon e^{i\theta}) d\theta \xrightarrow[\varepsilon \to 0]{} 2\pi i f(w)$,

and $\displaystyle\iint_{G_\varepsilon} \frac{f_{\bar{z}}}{z - w} dm \xrightarrow[\varepsilon \to 0]{} \iint_G \frac{f_{\bar{z}}}{z - w} dm$. Collecting terms, we have the lemma.

Two special cases of Lemma 3.1.2 are of interest: if $f_{\bar{z}} = 0$ in G, i.e., f is holomorphic, Lemma 3.1.2 is the Cauchy integral formula. The other special case is:

COROLLARY 3.1.3. *Let* $f \in C_c^{(1)}$. *Then for all* $w \in \mathbb{C}$,
$f(w) = \frac{1}{\pi} \displaystyle\int_{\mathbb{C}} \frac{f_{\bar{z}}}{w - z} dm.$

<u>Proof</u>. Take γ to be a large circle in Lemma 3.1.2.

We next derive some simple facts about compactly supported measures in the plane. (As usual, measure means complex Borel measure.)

DEFINITION. Let X be a compact set in $\mathbb{C}$, μ a measure on X. For all $w \in \mathbb{C}$, we put $\tilde{\mu}(w) = \int \frac{d|\mu|}{|w - z|}$.

LEMMA 3.1.4. *With* X, μ *as above,* $\tilde{\mu}$ *is summable (with respect to* m) *over any bounded set; in particular,* $\tilde{\mu} < \infty$ *a.e.* (m).

<u>Proof</u>. Let $D = \Delta(0; R)$. Then, by Lemma 3.1.1,

$$\int_X d|\mu|(w) \int_D \frac{dm(s)}{|w - s|} \leq 2\pi R|\mu|(X),$$

and $\frac{1}{|z_1 - z_2|}$ is obviously measurable with respect to the product measure $|\mu| \times m$ on $X \times D$, so Fubini's theorem applies, and yields the lemma.

DEFINITION. Let X, μ be as above. For each $w \in \mathbb{C}$ such that $\tilde{\mu}(w) < \infty$, we define

$$\hat{\mu}(w) = \int_X \frac{d\mu}{z - w}.$$

Thus $\hat{\mu}$ is defined a.e. (m), and summable over bounded sets; $|\hat{\mu}| \leq \tilde{\mu}$. We can make a stronger statement if μ is boundedly absolutely continuous with respect to m.

LEMMA 3.1.5. *Let* X *be a compact plane set,* g *a bounded Borel function on* X. *Let*

$$f(w) = \int_X \frac{g}{z - w}\, dm, \quad \textit{for all } w \in \mathbb{C}.$$

Then f *is continuous on* $\mathbb{C}$, *holomorphic in* $\mathbb{C}\setminus X$, *and vanishes at* ∞.

Proof. The last two assertions are trivial. That f is continuous is a special case of a well-known fact: the convolution of a bounded and a summable function is continuous. For completeness, we give the details. We may assume $m(X) = \|g\| = 1$. Let $\varepsilon > 0$. Choose R so $X \subset \Delta(0; R/2)$. Choose h, a continuous function with compact support, such that $\int_{\Delta(0;R)} |h - \frac{1}{z}|\, dm < \varepsilon$. Choose $\delta > 0$ such that $|h(s) - h(t)| < \varepsilon$ whenever $|s - t| < \delta$. Now for $|t| < R/2$,

$$\left| f(t) - \int_X g(s)h(s - t)\,dm(s) \right|$$

$$\leq \int_X |g(s)| \left| \frac{1}{s - t} - h(s - t) \right| dm(s)$$

$$\leq \|g\| \int_{\Delta(0;R)} \left| \frac{1}{z} - h \right| dm < \varepsilon.$$

Hence, if s, t $\in \Delta(0; R/2)$ and $|s - t| < \delta$, we have

$$|f(s) - f(t)|$$
$$< \varepsilon + \varepsilon + \int_X |g(u)||h(u-s) - h(u-t)|dm(u)$$
$$< 2\varepsilon + \|g\| dm(X) \sup\{|h(s) - h(t)|: |s-t| < \delta\}$$
$$< 3\varepsilon.$$

Thus f is (uniformly) continuous on $\Delta(0; R/2)$, and hence on all of $\mathbb{C}$. The proof is finished.

LEMMA 3.1.6. *Let* X *be a compact plane set,* μ *a measure on* X, $f \in C_c^{(1)}$. *Then*

$$\int_X f d\mu = \frac{1}{\pi} \int f_{\bar{z}}\, \hat{\mu}\, dm.$$

<u>Proof</u>. $\int_X f d\mu = \frac{1}{\pi} \int_X d\mu(w) \int_{\mathbb{C}} \frac{f_{\bar{z}}}{w - z} dm =$

$\frac{1}{\pi} \int_{\mathbb{C}} f_{\bar{z}}\, \hat{\mu} dm$ by Corollary 3.1.3 and Fubini's theorem.

COROLLARY 3.1.7. *Let* μ *be a measure on* $\mathbb{C}$ *with compact support. If* U *is an open set and* $\hat{\mu} = 0$ *a.e.* (m) *in* U, *then* $|\mu|(U) = 0$ *(i.e.,* supp $\mu \subset$ supp $\hat{\mu}m$). *In particular,* $\mu = 0$ *if and only if*

$\hat{\mu} = 0$ *a.e.* (m).

Proof. If $f \in C_c^{(1)}(U)$, then $\int f d\mu = 0$ by Lemma 3.1.6. If K is a compact subset of U, there exist $f_n \in C_c^{(1)}(U)$ decreasing to χ_K, so $\mu(K) = 0$. It follows from regularity that $|\mu|(U) = 0$.

In the language of distribution theory, Lemma 3.1.6 says that $\frac{\partial}{\partial \bar{z}} \hat{\mu} = -\pi\mu$. The next result is suggested by Leibniz's formula.

LEMMA 3.1.8. *Let* μ *be a measure on the compact set* $X \subset \mathbb{C}$, *and let* $h \in C_c^{(1)}$. *Put*

$$\nu = h\mu - \frac{1}{\pi} h_{\bar{z}} \hat{\mu} m.$$

Then the compactly supported measure ν *has the property*: $\hat{\nu} = h\hat{\mu}$.

Proof. Let w be any point where $\tilde{\mu}(w) < \infty$. Then

$$\hat{\nu}(w) = \int_X \frac{h d\mu}{z - w} - \frac{1}{\pi} \int_{\mathbb{C}} \frac{h_{\bar{z}}}{z - w} \hat{\mu} dm$$

$$= \int_X \left[\frac{1}{\pi} \int_{\mathbb{C}} \frac{h_{\bar{z}}(t)}{s - t} dm(t) \right] \frac{1}{s - w} d\mu(s)$$

$$- \frac{1}{\pi} \int_{\mathbb{C}} \frac{h_{\bar{z}}(t)}{t - w} \hat{\mu}(t) dm(t)$$

$$= \frac{1}{\pi}\int_{\mathbb{C}}\left[\int_X \frac{d\mu(s)}{(s-t)(s-w)} - \frac{\hat{\mu}(t)}{t-w}\right]h_{\bar{z}}(t)\,dm(t)$$

$$= \frac{1}{\pi}\int_{\mathbb{C}}\left[\frac{1}{t-w}\int_X\left(\frac{1}{s-t} - \frac{1}{s-w}\right)d\mu(s)\right.$$

$$\left. - \frac{\hat{\mu}(t)}{t-w}\right]h_{\bar{z}}(t)\,dm(t)$$

$$= \frac{1}{\pi}\int_{\mathbb{C}}\frac{h_{\bar{z}}(t)}{t-w}(\hat{\mu}(t) - \hat{\mu}(w) - \hat{\mu}(t))\,dm(t)$$

$$= \hat{\mu}(w)\,\frac{1}{\pi}\int_{\mathbb{C}}\frac{h_{\bar{z}}(t)}{w-t}\,dm(t) = h(w)\hat{\mu}(w),$$

as was to be proved.

Finally, we observe how to recover the atomic part of μ from $\hat{\mu}$ or $\tilde{\mu}$.

LEMMA 3.1.9. *Let* μ *be a compactly supported measure in the plane, let* $w \in \mathbb{C}$. *Put* $\Delta_n = \Delta(w; 1/n)$, *and* $c_n = m(\Delta_n)^{-1} = \frac{n^2}{\pi}$. *Then*

$$\mu(\{w\}) = \lim c_n \int_{\Delta_n}(w - z)\hat{\mu}\,dm, \text{ and}$$

$$|\mu(\{w\})| = \lim c_n \int_{\Delta_n}|w - z|\tilde{\mu}\,dm.$$

Proof. Let $F_n(s) = c_n \int_{\Delta_n}\frac{z - w}{z - s}\,dm$, and $G_n(s) = c_n \int_{\Delta_n}\left|\frac{z - w}{z - s}\right|\,dm$. Then $F_n(w) = G_n(w) = 1$, and

$|F_n| \le G_n$. If $s \neq w$, we have for $n > |s - w|^{-1}$,

$$\frac{1}{n}\left\|(z - s)^{-1}\right\|_{\Delta_n} \le \frac{1}{n}\left(|w - s| - \frac{1}{n}\right)^{-1},$$

so $G_n(s)$ (and hence $F_n(s)$) converges to 0. Also, $G_n(s) \le \frac{1}{n} c_n \int_{\Delta_n} \frac{dm}{|z - s|} \le 2$ by Lemma 3.1.1. Thus, F_n and G_n converge boundedly to $\chi_{\{w\}}$, and applying the dominated convergence theorem and Fubini's theorem, we have

$$\begin{aligned}\mu(\{w\}) &= \lim \int F_n d\mu \\ &= \lim c_n \int d\mu(s) \int \frac{t - w}{t - s}\, dm(t) \\ &= \lim c_n \int (w - t)\hat{\mu}(t)\, dm(t),\end{aligned}$$

and

$$\begin{aligned}|\mu(\{w\})| = |\mu|(\{x\}) &= \lim \int G_n\, d|\mu| \\ &= \lim c_n \int d|\mu|(s) \int \left|\frac{t - w}{t - s}\right| dm(t) \\ &= \lim c_n \int |z - w|\tilde{\mu}\, dm.\end{aligned}$$

3-2 ANNIHILATING MEASURES FOR R(X)

Throughout this section, X will denote a compact plane set. We recall from Chapter 1 that R(X) is the uniform closure on X of the rational functions with no poles on X, P(X) the uniform closure of the polynomials.

THEOREM 3.2.1. *Let* μ *be a measure on* X. *Then* $\mu \perp R(X)$ *if and only if* $\hat{\mu}$ *vanishes off* X.

Proof. If $w \notin X$, $\dfrac{1}{z - w} \in R(X)$, so $\hat{\mu}(w) = 0$ if $\mu \perp R(X)$. Suppose $\hat{\mu} = 0$ off X, and f is holomorphic in a neighborhood U of X. We can choose $h \in C_c^{(\infty)}(U)$ such that h = 1 in a neighborhood of X. Then

$$\int f d\mu = \int fh d\mu = \int_{\mathbb{C}} (fh)_{\bar{z}}\, \hat{\mu} dm$$

$$= \int_X (fh)_{\bar{z}}\, \hat{\mu} dm = \int_X f_{\bar{z}}\, \hat{\mu} dm = 0.$$

Thus μ annihilates the restriction of any function holomorphic in a neighborhood of X, in particular, any rational function whose poles lie off X, so $\mu \perp R(X)$.

As a bonus, we see that any function holomorphic in a neighborhood of X can be approximated uniformly on X by rational functions; even a slightly stronger statement is true:

COROLLARY 3.2.2. *Let* $f \in C^{(1)}(U)$ *for some neighborhood* U *of* X, *and suppose* $f_{\bar{z}} = 0$ *on* X. *Then* $f|X \in R(X)$.

Proof. We may assume that $f \in C_c^{(1)}(U)$. Then for all $\mu \perp R(X)$, $\int f d\mu = \frac{1}{\pi} \int_X f_{\bar{z}} \hat{\mu} dm = 0$, since $\hat{\mu} = 0$ off X by Theorem 3.2.1. Hence $f|X \in R(X)$.

We can use measures to prove Runge's theorem, for which we outlined a constructive proof in Chapter 1, Section 4.

THEOREM 3.2.3. *Let* $G_1, G_2, \ldots$ *be the bounded connected components of* $\mathbb{C}\backslash X$, *and let* $a_n \in G_n$ *for each* n. *Then any function holomorphic in a neighborhood of* X *can be approximated uniformly on* X *by rational functions with poles only among the* $\{a_n\}$. *In particular, if* X *has connected complement, any function holomorphic in a neighborhood of* X *is uniformly approximable on* X *by polynomials.*

Proof. Let B be the function algebra on X generated by z and by $\{\frac{1}{z - a_n} : n = 1, 2, \ldots\}$. Clearly, $B \subset R(X)$, and the assertion is that $B = R(X)$. Let μ be a measure on X which annihilates B. Then $\hat{\mu}$ is holomorphic off X, $\hat{\mu}(a_n) = \int \frac{d\mu}{z - a_n} = 0$, and $\hat{\mu}^{(k)}(a_n) = k! \int \frac{d\mu}{(z - a_n)^k} = 0$ for every n, k. It follows that $\hat{\mu}$ vanishes in a neighborhood of each a_n, hence throughout G_n for each n. Now for any w, $|w| > \max\{|s| : s \in X\}$, we have $\frac{1}{z - w} = -\sum_0^\infty \frac{z^n}{w^{n+1}}$, the series converging uniformly on X, and since $\int z^n d\mu = 0$ for all n, it follows that $\hat{\mu}(w) = 0$. Hence $\hat{\mu}$ vanishes on the whole unbounded component of $\mathbb{C}\setminus X$. Thus $\hat{\mu} = 0$ off X, so $\mu \perp R(X)$. The theorem follows.

The next corollary of Theorem 3.2.1 is known as the Hartogs-Rosenthal theorem.

THEOREM 3.2.4. *If* $m(X) = 0$, *then* $R(X) = C(X)$.

Proof. Let $\mu \perp R(X)$. By Theorem 3.2.1, $\hat{\mu} = 0$ off X, so $\hat{\mu} = 0$ a.e. (m), and by Corollary 3.1.7 it follows that $\mu = 0$. Hence $R(X) = C(X)$.

Constructive proofs of Theorems 3.2.2 and 3.2.4 are easy to obtain. If $f \in C^{(1)}(U)$, where U is a neighborhood of X, choose an open set G with smooth boundary γ such that $X \subset G \subset \overline{G} \subset U$. If either $f_{\bar{z}} = 0$ on X or $m(X) = 0$, we can choose G so that for $w \in X$, $\left|\int_G \frac{f_{\bar{z}}}{z - w}\, dm\right|$ is arbitrarily small (it suffices to take $m(G\backslash X)$ small, by Lemma 3.1.1). Now if $g(w) = \int_\gamma \frac{f dz}{z - w}$, then $g \in R(X)$ by an argument given in 1.4 (the approximating sums are rational functions of w), and 3.2.2 and 3.2.4 then follow from Lemma 3.1.2.

Theorem 3.2.4 is totally unimpressive unless one realizes that there are compact sets X with empty interior for which $R(X) \neq C(X)$. Here is the crucial example, known as the *Swiss cheese*, for reasons which will be apparent.

Start with a closed disk D_0, and choose a countable family $\{D_n\}$ of open disks, such that: i) $\overline{D}_n \subset \operatorname{int} D_0$, for each n; ii) $\overline{D}_n \cap \overline{D}_m$ is empty for $n \neq m$; iii) $D_0 \backslash \bigcup_1^\infty D_n$ has empty interior; and iv) $\sum_1^\infty r_n < \infty$, where r_n is the radius of D_n. (It is easy to define such D_n inductively, with centers chosen from any dense subset $\{a_n\}$ of int D_0, and radii from any given sequence $\{\varepsilon_n\}$ with $\varepsilon_n > 0$ and $\Sigma\, \varepsilon_n < \infty$.) Let $X = D_0 \backslash \bigcup_1^\infty D_n$, so X is a compact set with empty interior. Let γ_n be the boundary of D_n.

Since $\int_{\gamma_n} |dz| = 2\pi r_n$, and $\Sigma\, r_n < \infty$, it follows that $\sum_1^\infty \int_{\gamma_n} f dz$ converges absolutely for any $f \in C(X)$. Thus there is a measure μ on X, which we may describe by: if $f \in C(X)$, $\int f d\mu = \int_{\gamma_0} f dz - \sum_1^\infty \int_{\gamma_n} f dz$. Evidently, $\mu \neq 0$, in fact $\| \mu \| = 2\pi \sum_0^\infty r_n$. If f is a rational function whose poles lie off X, then all the poles of f are contained in $\bigcup_1^N D_n$, for some N. From the Cauchy theorem, it follows that $\int_{\gamma_0} f dz - \sum_1^n \int_{\gamma_k} f dz = 0$ for all $n \geq N$, and hence that $\int f d\mu = 0$. Hence $\mu \perp R(X)$, and hence $R(X) \neq C(X)$.

Evidently, in this construction one may replace disks by Jordan regions with rectifiable boundary; then iv) becomes $\Sigma\, \ell_n < \infty$, where ℓ_n is the length of γ_n.

A consequence of the Hartogs-Rosenthal theorem is that the Swiss Cheese has positive plane measure. William Allard has given the following direct argument for this unobvious fact. We can assume D_0 is the unit disk. For each $x \in [-1, 1]$, let $I_n(x)$ be the number of points on the circle γ_n which meet the line $\{s : \text{Re } s = x\}$; thus $I_n(x) = 0, 1$, or 2.

It is trivial that for each n, $\int_{-1}^{1} I_n(x)dx = 4r_n$. Hence, $\sum_1^\infty \int_{-1}^{1} I_n(x)dx < \infty$, so by the monotone convergence (or Beppo Levi) theorem, $\int_{-1}^{1} \sum_1^\infty I_n(x)dx < \infty$, and in particular, $\sum_1^\infty I_n(x) < \infty$ for almost all $x \in [-1, 1]$. Thus, for almost all x, $I_n(x) = 0$ for all but finitely many n, so $X_x = \{s \in X : \text{Re } s = x\}$ is a finite union of non-degenerate intervals. In particular, X_x has positive one-dimensional measure for almost all x, and hence $m(X) > 0$ by Fubini's theorem.

We now begin an examination of R(X) as a function algebra, and see how the various definitions and theorems of Chapter 2 fit in.

LEMMA 3.2.5. *Let* K *be a peak set for* R(X). *Then* $R(X)|K = R(K)$.

Proof. Let G be a bounded component of $\mathbb{C}\setminus K$. Then G meets $\mathbb{C}\setminus X$: for if $G \subset X$, and f peaks on K, $f \in R(X)$, then f is holomorphic in G and equals 1 on the boundary of G, hence f = 1 in G, a contradiction. It follows from Theorem 3.2.3 that $R(X)|K$ is dense in R(K). Since K is a peak set, $R(X)|K$ is closed (Theorem 2.4.3), and the proof is finished.

COROLLARY 3.2.6. *Let* $X = \cup X_\alpha$ *be the decomposition of* X *into maximal sets of antisymmetry for* $R(X)$. *Then* $R(X)|X_\alpha = R(X_\alpha)$ *for every* α, *and* X_α *reduces to a singleton for all but countably many* α.

<u>Proof</u>. Since each X_α is a peak set, the first assertion is a consequence of Lemma 3.2.5. Since $R(X)|X_\alpha$ is antisymmetric, the second now follows from the Hartogs-Rosenthal theorem.

COROLLARY 3.2.7. *Let* E *be the essential set for* $R(X)$. *Then* $R(X) = \{f \in C(X) : f|E \in R(E)\}$.

<u>Proof</u>. Immediate from Theorem 2.8.1 and Lemma 3.2.5.

The next simple observation can be very useful.

LEMMA 3.2.8. *Let* $\mu \perp R(X)$, *and* $h \in C_c^{(1)}$. *Then there exists* $\nu \perp R(X)$ *such that* $\hat{\nu} = h\hat{\mu}$, *and* $\text{supp}\ \nu \subset X \cap \text{supp}\ h$.

<u>Proof</u>. Let $\nu = h\mu - \frac{1}{\pi} h_{\bar{z}}\, \hat{\mu}m$. By Lemma 3.1.8, $\hat{\nu} = h\hat{\mu}$, and by Lemma 3.2.1, $\nu \perp R(X)$.

The last two results allow us to strengthen

Corollary 3.2.2.

THEOREM 3.2.9. *Let* E *be the essential set for* R(X). *Let* $f \in C^{(1)}(U)$ *for some neighborhood* U *of* X. *Then* $f|X \in R(X)$ *if and only if* $f_{\bar{z}} = 0$ *on* E.

Proof. Suppose $f_{\bar{z}} = 0$ on E. For any $\mu \perp R(X)$, we have supp $\mu \subset E$ and $\hat{\mu} = 0$ off E, by Lemma 3.2.5 and Theorem 3.2.1, so $\int f d\mu = \frac{1}{\pi} \int f_{\bar{z}}\, \hat{\mu}\, dm = 0$. It follows that $f \in R(X)$.

Now suppose $f \in R(X)$. Let $K = \{w \in X : f_{\bar{z}}(w) = 0\}$. For any $\mu \perp R(X)$, we have $\int f_{\bar{z}}\, \hat{\mu} dm = \pi \int f d\mu = 0$. Hence, by Lemma 3.2.8, $\int f_{\bar{z}} h \hat{\mu} dm = 0$ for all $\mu \perp R(X)$, all $h \in C_c^{(1)}$. Thus $f_{\bar{z}}\hat{\mu} = 0$ a.e. (m), for any $\mu \perp R(X)$, and hence $\hat{\mu} = 0$ a.e. (m) on $\mathbb{C} \backslash K$, so $\mu \perp R(K)$. Since this holds for any $\mu \perp R(X)$, it follows that $R(X) \supset \{f \in C(X) : f|K \in R(K)\}$ and so $K \supset E$, and the theorem is proved.

Theorem 3.2.9 enables us to put some limitations on the real functions in R(X).

THEOREM 3.2.10. *Let* $f \in C^2(U)$, *where* U *is a neighborhood of* X, *and suppose that* $f|X \in R(X)$ *and* $f|X$ *is real. Then* f *is constant on each component of the essential set* E *for* R(X). *In particular, if* X *is connected and* R(X) *is essential, there exist no non-constant smooth real-valued functions in* R(X).

Proof. We can assume f is real in U. By Theorem 3.2.9, $f_{\bar{z}} = 0$ on E, and hence (since f is real) $f_z = 0$ on E, as well. Thus f(E) is a set of critical values of f. It follows from the Morse-Sard theorem (see, e.g., Sternberg, "Lectures on Differential Geometry", Prentice-Hall, 1964) that f(E) has linear measure zero. In particular, f(K) is a connected null set of reals for each connected subset K of E; and the theorem is proved.

One might conjecture that if X is connected and R(X) essential, then R(X) is antisymmetric. However, Steen [1] has constructed a Swiss cheese X such that R(X) is not antisymmetric (it is clear that any Swiss cheese is connected, and R(X) is essential). The non-constant real f $\in$ R(X) which Steen displays is given by f(s) = F(Re s), where F is the familiar Cantor function on the line; thus f is differentiable a.e. (m), which shows the limitations of Theorem 3.2.10.

From Lemma 3.2.8 we can also deduce a local

maximum modulus principle for $R(X)$.

THEOREM 3.2.11. *Let* $s \in X$, U *a neighborhood of* s, *and suppose there exists* $f \in R(X)$ *such that* $|f(s)| > |f(t)|$ *for all* $t \in U \cap X$. *Then* s *is a peak point for* $R(X)$.

Proof. As we saw in Chapter 2, if s is not a peak point, there is a representing measure for s other than δ_s, and hence there exists $\mu \perp R(X)$ with $\mu(\{s\}) \neq 0$. We show this is impossible with our hypothesis. Choose $h \in C_c^{(1)}(U)$ such that $h = 1$ in a neighborhood of s. Put $\nu = h\mu - \frac{1}{\pi} h_{\bar{z}}\hat{\mu}m$. Then $\nu \perp R(X)$, as we have seen, and $\nu(\{s\}) = \mu(\{s\})$. We may assume that $f(s) = 1$. Then $f^n \to \chi_{\{s\}}$ boundedly on supp $\nu \subset U \cap X$, so we have $\mu(\{s\}) = \nu(\{s\}) = \lim \int f^n d\nu = 0$. The theorem is proved.

This theorem admits a generalization to arbitrary function algebras, one of the genuinely deep results of the subject. It was found by Rossi, and asserts: *let* A *be a function algebra on* $X = \text{Spec } A$. *Suppose* K *is a closed subset of* X, U *a neighborhood of* K, *with* K *a peak set for* $A|U$. *Then* K *is a peak set for* A.

For a proof of Rossi's local maximum modulus principle, we refer the reader to the book of Gunning and Rossi [1], where it is proved in the first chapter. See also Stolzenberg [2] and Hörmander [1].

Our next lemma is due to Bishop [1]. The proof we give was suggested by Hoffman.

LEMMA 3.2.12. *Let* $\mu \perp R(X)$, *and let* $U_1,\ldots,U_n$ *be open sets with* $X \subset \bigcup_1^n U_j$. *Then there exist* $\mu_j \perp R(X)$, $1 \leq j \leq n$, *with* $\operatorname{supp} \mu_j \subset U_j$, $\operatorname{supp} \hat{\mu}_j \subset U_j$ *for each* j, *and* $\mu = \sum_1^n \mu_j$.

Proof. Choose $h_j \in C_c^{(1)}(U_j)$ such that $\Sigma h_j = 1$ in a neighborhood of X (i.e., a partition of unity subordinate to the cover $\{U_j\}$). Choose $\mu_j \perp R(X)$, so that $\hat{\mu}_j = h_j\hat{\mu}$ and $\operatorname{supp} \mu_j \subset U_j$ (Lemma 3.2.8). Then $\hat{\mu} = (\Sigma h_j)\hat{\mu} = \Sigma(h_j\hat{\mu}) = \Sigma \hat{\mu}_j = (\Sigma \mu_j)\hat{}$, so $\mu = \Sigma \mu_j$ by Lemma 3.1.7. The lemma is proven.

THEOREM 3.2.13. *Suppose* $f \in C(X)$, *and suppose each point of* X *has a neighborhood* V *in* X *such that* $f|\overline{V} \in R(\overline{V})$. *Then* $f \in R(X)$.

<u>Proof</u>. From the compactness of X, we can find open U_j, $1 \leq j \leq n$, such that $X \subset \bigcup_1^n U_j$, and $V_j = U_j \cap X$ has the property: $f|\overline{V}_j \in R(\overline{V}_j)$. For any $\mu \perp R(X)$, write $\mu = \sum_1^n \mu_j$ as in Lemma 3.2.12. Then $\int f d\mu = \sum \int f d\mu_j = 0$, so $f \in R(X)$.

This last theorem answers for R(X) a question that can be raised for any function algebra. We make the definition:

A function algebra A on X is called *local* if whenever $V_1, \ldots, V_n$ is an open cover of X, $f \in C(X)$ and $f|V_j \in A|V_j$ for $1 \leq j \leq n$, then $f \in A$.

The question is: if X = Spec A, does it follow that A is local? For R(X), as we have just seen, the answer is yes; in fact, R(X) has the stronger property of being "approximately local", the definition of which we leave to the reader. However, for the general case, the answer is *no*. The counter-example was found by Eva Kallin [1]; it is P(X) for a certain polynomially convex $X \subset \mathbb{C}^4$.

3-3 REPRESENTING MEASURES FOR R(X)

Throughout this section, X denotes a compact plane set.

Let $x \in X$. If ν is a (complex) measure which represents x for $R(X)$, then $(z - x)\nu$ obviously annihilates $R(X)$. The very useful converse of this remark is due to Bishop, and we formulate it as a theorem.

THEOREM 3.3.1. *Let* $\mu \perp R(X)$, *If* $x \in X$, $\tilde{\mu}(x) < \infty$, *and* $\hat{\mu}(x) \neq 0$, *then* $\nu = \dfrac{1}{\hat{\mu}(x)} \dfrac{\mu}{z - x}$ *is a complex measure which represents* x.

Proof. Since $\tilde{\mu}(x) < \infty$, the measure ν is well-defined. Evidently, $\int d\nu = 1$. If f is a rational function whose poles lie off X, so is $\dfrac{f - f(x)}{z - x}$, so $\int \dfrac{f - f(x)}{z - x} d\mu = 0$. Thus, for such f,

$$f(x) = \int f(x) d\nu = \int [f - (f - f(x))] d\nu$$

$$= \int f d\nu - \frac{1}{\hat{\mu}(x)} \int \frac{f - f(x)}{z - x} d\mu = \int f d\nu,$$

and hence $f(x) = \int f d\nu$ for all $f \in R(X)$. The theorem is proved.

COROLLARY 3.3.2. *Let* $x \in X$. *Then* x *is a peak point for* $R(X)$ *if and only if* $\hat{\mu}(x) = 0$ *whenever* $\mu \perp R(X)$ *and* $\tilde{\mu}(x) < \infty$.

Proof. If there exists $\mu \perp R(X)$ with $\tilde{\mu}(x) < \infty$ and $\hat{\mu}(x) \neq 0$, Theorem 3.3.1 shows that there exists a measure ν representing x with $\nu(\{x\}) = 0$. As we saw in Chapter 2, this implies that x is not a peak point (recall: if f peaks at x, then $f^n \to \chi_{\{x\}}$ boundedly, so $1 = f^n(x) = \int f^n d\nu \to \nu(\{x\})$ whenever ν represents x).

On the other hand, if x is not a peak point, there exists a representing measure λ for x with $\lambda(\{x\}) = 0$ (Theorem 2.3.4). Then $\mu = (z - x)\lambda \perp R(X)$, and $\hat{\mu}(x) = \tilde{\mu}(x) = 1$. The proof is finished.

The "only if" part of the above immediately yields a theorem of Bishop [2]:

THEOREM 3.3.3. $R(X) = C(X)$ *if and only if almost all* (m) *points of* X *are peak points for* R(X).

Proof. If almost all (m) points of X are peak points, Corollary 3.3.2 shows that for all $\mu \perp R(X)$, $\hat{\mu} = 0$ a.e. on X, and hence (3.2.1) $\hat{\mu} = 0$ a.e., and hence $\mu = 0$. Thus $R(X) = C(X)$. The other direction is obvious, so the proof is complete.

This argument of Bishop's also has the following formulation:

THEOREM 3.3.4. *Let* E *be the essential set for* $R(X)$, B *the minimal boundary (set of all peak points). Then* E *is the closure of* $X\backslash B$.

<u>Proof</u>. Let F be the closure of $X\backslash B$. Since $X\backslash E$ consists of peak points, $X\backslash E \subset B$, so $E \supset X\backslash B$, and hence $E \supset F$. On the other hand, if $\mu \perp R(X)$, we have $\hat{\mu} = 0$ a.c. on $X\backslash F$ by Corollary 3.3.2, so $\mu \perp R(F)$ by Theorem 3.2.1. Thus $R(X) \supset \{f \in C(X) : f|F \in R(F)\}$, so $F \supset E$. The theorem is proved.

With Theorem 3.3.4, we can obtain another proof of the "only if" part of Theorem 3.2.9, in fact, a slightly stronger result.

LEMMA 3.3.5. *Suppose* $f \in R(X)$ *is differentiable at* $x \in X$. *Then either* x *is a peak point, or* $f_{\bar{z}}(x) = 0$.

<u>Proof</u>. Recall the definition of differentiable: there exist $a, b \in \mathbb{C}$ ($a = f_z(x)$, $b = f_{\bar{z}}(x)$) such that $f = f(x) + a(z - x) + b(\bar{z} - \bar{x}) + g$, where $|y - x|^{-1}|g(y)| \to 0$ as $y \to x$ in X. If $b \neq 0$, put $h = b^{-1}(z - x)[f - f(x) - a(z - x)]$; then $h \in R(X)$.

Since $h = |z - x|^2 + b^{-1}(z - x)g$, we see that $\mathrm{Re}\, h > 0$ in some punctured neighborhood of x, while $h(x) = 0$. Hence $e^{-h} \in R(X)$ peaks at x, relative to a neighborhood of x. The lemma now follows from Theorem 3.2.11.

> The argument used here was employed by Wermer [6] to obtain a much deeper theorem.

COROLLARY 3.3.6. *Let* $f \in R(X)$, *and suppose* f *differentiable at each point of* X. *Then the closure of* $\{x: f_{\bar{z}}(x) = 0\}$ *contains the essential set for* R(X).

<u>Proof</u>. Immediate from Lemma 3.3.5 and Theorem 3.3.4.

We can apply Theorem 3.3.1 to the study of the Gleason parts, and more generally, the norm topology on X induced by R(X). The next result was found by Wilken [1].

THEOREM 3.3.7. *If* x *is not a peak point for* R(X), *the Gleason part of* x *has positive measure.*

<u>Proof</u>. If x is not a peak point, there exists a positive representing measure λ for x with $\lambda(\{x\}) =$

0. Let $\mu = (z - x)\lambda$. Then $\mu \perp R(X)$, and $\mu \neq 0$. Let $Y = \{y \in X: \tilde{\mu}(y) < \infty \text{ and } \hat{\mu}(y) \neq 0\}$. If $y \in Y$, $\nu = \frac{1}{\hat{\mu}(y)} \frac{\mu}{z - y}$ is a complex measure which represents y; by Theorem 2.1.1, there exists a positive representing measure for y absolutely continuous with respect to ν, and therefore absolutely continuous with respect to λ. It follows that y belongs to the Gleason part of x. Since $m(Y) > 0$ by Lemma 3.1.4 and Corollary 3.1.7, the theorem is proved.

Wilken has extended this argument to show that if x is not a peak point for R(X), then x is in fact a point of density for its Gleason part. Melnikov [2] has a proof of this fact using the tools of analytic capacity. The author [2] found (independently) a slightly more general result, which has some interesting corollaries. This result (Theorem 3.3.9 below) can also be obtained by Melnikov's arguments.

We denote by $\|x - y\|$ (for x, $y \in X$) the distance between the associated functionals on R(X), i.e., $\|x - y\| = \sup\{|f(x) - f(y)| : \|f\| \leq 1, f \in R(X)\}$. Then the Gleason part of x is

$\{y: \|x - y\| < 2\}$.

THEOREM 3.3.8. *Let* $x \in X$, *let* μ *be a measure which represents* x, *let* $\varepsilon > 0$, *and let* $\delta = \dfrac{\varepsilon}{\|\mu\| + 1 + \varepsilon}$. *Then* $\|y - x\| < \varepsilon$ *whenever* $|y - x|\tilde{\mu}(y) < \delta$.

Proof. Since $(z-x)\mu \perp R(X)$, the measure $\dfrac{1}{c}\dfrac{z - x}{z - y}\mu$, with $c = \int \dfrac{z - x}{z - y}\, d\mu$, represents y whenever $c \neq 0$, and $\tilde{\mu}(y) < \infty$. But $c = \int \dfrac{z - y - (x - y)}{z - y}\, d\mu = 1 - (x - y)\hat{\mu}(y)$, so $|c| \geq 1 - |x - y|\tilde{\mu}(y) > 0$ when y satisfies the hypothesis of the lemma, since $\delta < 1$. Thus

$$\|x - y\| \leq \int \left| \frac{1}{c}\frac{z - x}{z - y} - 1\right| d|\mu|$$

$$= \int \left| \frac{z - x - cz + cy - y + y}{c(z - y)} \right| d|\mu|$$

$$= \frac{1}{|c|} \int \left| \frac{(1 - c)(z - y) + y - x}{z - y}\right| d|\mu|$$

$$= \frac{1}{|c|} \int \left| (x - y) \left[\hat{\mu}(y) - \frac{1}{z - y}\right] \right| d|\mu|$$

$$\leq \frac{|x - y|}{|c|} \left(|\hat{\mu}(y)|\, \|\mu\| + \tilde{\mu}(y)\right)$$

$$\leq \frac{|x - y|\tilde{\mu}(y)}{1 - |x - y|\tilde{\mu}(y)} (\|\mu\| + 1)$$

$$< \frac{\delta}{1 - \delta} (\|\mu\| + 1) = \varepsilon.$$

THEOREM 3.3.9. *Let* $P_\varepsilon = \{y \in X: \|y - x\| < \varepsilon\}$, *and let* $\Delta_n = \{y \in ¢ : |y - x| < \frac{1}{n}\}$. *If* $x \in X$ *is not a peak point, and* $\varepsilon > 0$, *then*

$$\frac{m(P_\varepsilon \cap \Delta_n)}{m(\Delta_n)} \to 1 \quad \textit{as} \quad n \to \infty.$$

Proof. Let μ be a measure which represents x such that $\mu(\{x\}) = 0$. Let $\delta = \dfrac{\varepsilon}{\|\mu\| + 1 + \varepsilon}$. According to the last Lemma, $P_\varepsilon \supset \{y \in ¢ : |x - y|\tilde{\mu}(y) < \delta\}$, so $m(P_\varepsilon \cap \Delta_n) \geq m\{y \in \Delta_n : |x - y|\tilde{\mu}(y) < \delta\}$

$$\geq m(\Delta_n) - \frac{1}{\delta}\int_{\Delta_n} |x - z|\tilde{\mu}dm$$

so

$$1 \geq \frac{m(P_\varepsilon \cap \Delta_n)}{m(\Delta_n)} \geq 1 - \frac{1}{\delta}\frac{1}{m(\Delta_n)}\int_{\Delta_n} |x - z|\tilde{\mu}dm.$$

But according to Lemma 3.1.9,

$$\frac{1}{m(\Delta_n)}\int |z - x|\tilde{\mu}dm \to |\mu(\{x\})| = 0$$

as $n \to \infty$. This proves the theorem.

An immediate consequence is

COROLLARY 3.3.10. *The isolated points of* X, *in the norm topology, are precisely the peak points for* R(X).

Using results from Chapter 1, we get

COROLLARY 3.3.11. *Let* x ∈ X. *There exists a non-zero point derivation on* R(X) *at* x *if and only if* x *is not a peak point for* R(X).

Proof. Apply Corollary 3.3.10, and Theorem 1.6.5 with Corollary 1.6.4.

Thus, by Bishop's Theorem 3.3.3, R(X) admits non-zero point derivations at many points whenever R(X) ≠ C(X). For bounded point derivations, the situation is different. Wermer [7] has constructed a Swiss cheese X such that R(X) admits no non-zero bounded point derivations. In the same paper, he constructs Swiss cheeses with non-zero bounded point derivations at almost all points. Hallstrom [1] has given a necessary and sufficient condition for a point x ∈ X to admit a non-zero bounded point derivation. This condition uses the notion of analytic capacity, and is analogous to a condition, due to Melnikov [1], which is necessary and sufficient for x to be a peak point. For Melnikov's work, we refer the reader to Zalcman [1], and Curtis [1], where a significant simplification is made. Hallstrom's paper also contains many other interesting results concerning bounded point derivations, and derivations of higher order, on $R(X)$ and $A(X)$.

3-4 HARMONIC FUNCTIONS

In this section, we use the symbol Δ to denote the Laplace operator: $\Delta f = 4f_{z\bar{z}}$. A function of class $C^{(2)}$ is *harmonic* if $\Delta f = 0$. We begin with some analogues of the results obtained in Section 3-1.

LEMMA 3.4.1. *Let* $f \in C_c^{(2)}$. *Then for every* $w \in \mathbb{C}$,

$$f(w) = \frac{1}{2\pi} \int \log|z - w| \Delta f \, dm.$$

<u>Proof</u>. Choose R large enough so that $\operatorname{supp} f \subset \Delta(w; R)$. Let $G_\varepsilon = \{s : \varepsilon < |s - w| < R\}$, let γ_ε be the positively oriented circle of radius ε and center w. By Green's theorem, we have

$$\begin{aligned} - i \int_{\gamma_\varepsilon} f_{\bar{z}} \log|z - w| d\bar{z} &= 2 \int_{G_\varepsilon} \frac{\partial}{\partial z} (f_{\bar{z}} \log|z - w|) \, dm \\ &= 2 \int_{G_\varepsilon} f_{\bar{z}z} \log|z - w| dm + \int_{G_\varepsilon} \frac{f_{\bar{z}}}{z - w} \, dm. \end{aligned}$$

Now $\Delta f = 4f_{\bar{z}z}$, and the line integral above is of the order of $\varepsilon \log \varepsilon$, so letting $\varepsilon \to 0$ we have

$$\frac{1}{2\pi}\int \log|z - w|dm = \frac{1}{\pi}\int \frac{f_{\bar{z}}}{w - z}\, dm = f(w).$$

Since $\log|z - w|$ is summable (m) over compact sets for any w, an application of Fubini's theorem yields:

LEMMA 3.4.2. *Let* μ *be a compactly supported measure on* $\mathbb{C}$. *Then for almost all* (m) w, $\log|z - w| \in L^1(|\mu|)$, *and* $w \to \int \log|z - w|d|\mu|$ *is summable over compact sets.*

DEFINITION. If μ is a compactly supported measure on $\mathbb{C}$, we put

$$\check{\mu}(w) = \int \log|z - w|d\mu$$

for each w such that the integral is absolutely convergent. Thus $\check{\mu}$ is defined a.e. (m) and summable over compact sets.

LEMMA 3.4.3. *Let* μ *be a compactly supported measure, and* $f \in C_c^{(2)}$. *Then* $\int f d\mu = \frac{1}{2\pi}\int \Delta f\, \check{\mu}\, dm$.

<u>Proof</u>. Immediate from Lemma 3.4.1 and Fubini's theorem.

COROLLARY 3.4.4. *Let* μ *be a compactly supported measure. Then* supp $\mu \subset$ supp $\check{\mu}m$; *in particular,* $\mu = 0$ *if and only if* $\check{\mu} = 0$ *a.e.* (m).

Proof. Immediate from Lemma 3.4.3.

DEFINITION. If X is a compact plane set, we denote by H(X) the set of all real-valued continuous functions on X which are uniformly approximable on X by functions harmonic in a neighborhood of X. We put $H_b(X) = H(X)|\partial X$.

Since each $f \in H(X)$ is harmonic in int X, the maximum principle for harmonic functions shows that H(X) and $H_b(X)$ are isometrically isomorphic. We now look at annihilating and representing measures for H(X).

LEMMA 3.4.5. *Let* μ *be a real measure on the compact plane set* X. *Then* $\mu \perp H(X)$ *if and only if* $\check{\mu} = 0$ *off* X.

Proof. If $\mu \perp H(X)$, then $\check{\mu}(w) = 0$ for every $w \notin X$, since $\log|z - w|$ is harmonic in a neighborhood of X. If $\check{\mu} = 0$ off X, and f is harmonic in a neighborhood U of X, choose $\phi \in C_c^{(2)}(U)$ with $\phi = 1$ in a neighborhood of X. Then

$$\int f d\mu = \int f\phi d\mu = \frac{1}{2\pi}\int \check{\mu}\Delta(f\phi)dm = 0$$

since $\Delta(f\phi) = 0$ on X and $\check{\mu} = 0$ off X.

LEMMA 3.4.6. *Let* X *be a compact plane set, let* $G_1, G_2, \ldots,$ *be the bounded complementary components of* X, *let* $a_j \in G_j$ *for each* j. *Then the real measure* μ *on* X *annihilates* H(X) *if and only if* $\mu \perp R(X)$ *and* $\check{\mu}(a_j) = 0$ *for every* j.

Proof. If $f \in R(X)$, then Re f and Im $f \in H(X)$, so "only if" is immediate.

Suppose $\mu \perp R(X)$ and $\check{\mu}(a_j) = 0$ for every j. Then $\hat{\mu} = 0$ off X by Theorem 3.2.1. Differentiating under the integral sign, we find $\hat{\mu} = 2\frac{\partial\check{\mu}}{\partial z}$ off X; since $\check{\mu}$ is real, it follows that $\check{\mu}$ is constant on each component of $\mathbb{C}\setminus X$. Since $\check{\mu}(a_j) = 0$ for each j, $\check{\mu}$ vanishes in $\bigcup_1^\infty G_j$. Since $\log(z - w) \in R(X)$ if $|w|$ is sufficiently large, $\check{\mu}$ vanishes in the unbounded component of $\mathbb{C}\setminus X$. Thus $\check{\mu} = 0$ off X, and the lemma follows from Lemma 3.4.5.

COROLLARY 3.4.7. *Let* X, $\{a_j\}$ *be as in Lemma* 3.4.6.

Then the set of all finite linear combinations $\mathrm{Re}\, f + \Sigma\, c_j \log|z - a_j|$, *with* $f \in R(X)$ *and* c_j *real constants, is dense in* $H(X)$. *In particular, if* $\mathbb{C}\backslash X$ *is connected, then* $\mathrm{Re}\, P(X)$ *is dense in* $H(X)$.

Proof. Immediate from Lemma 3.4.6.

COROLLARY 3.4.8. *Let* X *be a compact plane set,* μ *a probability measure on* X. *Then* μ *is a representing measure for* $x \in X$ *with respect to* $H(X)$ *if and only if* μ *is an Arens-Singer measure for* x *with respect to* $R(X)$.

Proof. If f and f^{-1} belong to $R(X)$, then $\log|f| \in H(X)$, so a representing measure with respect to $H(X)$ must be an Arens-Singer measure with respect to $R(X)$. The other direction follows from Corollary 3.4.7.

We next take up the question of finding sufficient conditions in order that $H_b(X) = C_R(\partial X)$. It is clear that a necessary condition is that for each $x \in \partial X$, δ_x is the only Arens-Singer measure for X with respect to $R(X)$, and *a fortiori*, the only Jensen measure. We shall prove the converse of this fact. The proof uses the solvability of the

Dirichlet problem for smoothly bounded sets, and we first give a proof of this well-known result by methods in the spirit of this chapter.

LEMMA 3.4.9. *Let* X *be a smoothly bounded compact plane set, let* $w_0 \in \partial X$. *Then there exist* $w_n \in \mathbb{C}\backslash X$, $w_n \to w_0$, *and a constant* k *such that* $\log|w_n - z| > \log|w_0 - z| + k$ *on* X.

Proof. There exists a neighborhood U of w_0 such that $U\backslash X$ contains a sector, and hence a sequence $w_n \in U\backslash X$, $w_n \to w_0$, such that $\left|\arg \dfrac{w_n - w_0}{w - w_0}\right| \geq \delta > 0$ for all $w \in U \cap X$. It follows that

$$\left|\frac{w_n - w}{w_0 - w}\right| = \left|\frac{w_n - w_0 + w_0 - w}{w_0 - w}\right|$$

$$= \left|1 - \frac{w_n - w_0}{w - w_0}\right| \geq \sin\delta > 0,$$

and hence $\log|w_n - w| \geq \log|w_0 - w| + \log\sin\delta$ for all $w \in U \cap X$. Since $\log|w_n - z|$ converges uniformly to $\log|w_0 - z|$ on $X\backslash U$, the lemma is proved.

THEOREM 3.4.10. *Let* X *be a smoothly bounded compact plane set. Then* $H_b(X) = C_R(\partial X)$.

Proof. Let μ be a real measure on ∂X which annihilates $H(X)$. We must show $\mu = 0$, which by Corollary 3.4.4 is equivalent to showing $\check{\mu} = 0$ a.e. From Lemma 3.4.5, we know that $\check{\mu} = 0$ outside X, and ∂X has measure 0 since X is smoothly bounded, so it suffices to show that $\check{\mu}(\xi) = 0$ for any interior point ξ of X. Let ξ be such a point, and let λ be a representing measure for ξ with respect to $H(X)$. Then for any $w_0 \in \partial X$, choosing $\{w_n\}$ by Lemma 3.4.9, we have $\check{\lambda}(w_n) = \log|\xi - w_n|$, and

$$\begin{aligned}\int \log|z - w_0|\,d\lambda &\geq \lim \int \log|z - w_n|\,d\lambda \\ &= \log|\xi - w_0| > -\infty\end{aligned}$$

by Fatou's lemma, so $\log|z - w_0| \in L^1(\lambda)$, so $\check{\lambda}(w_0) = \log|\xi - w_0|$ by dominated convergence (Lemma 3.4.9). Then

$$\begin{aligned}\int d|\mu|(w) \int \log|z - w|\,d\lambda &= \int \log|\xi - w|\,d|\mu|(w) \\ &> -\infty,\end{aligned}$$

so by Fubini's theorem, $\check{\mu}(w) \in L^1(\lambda)$. Again applying Lemma 3.4.9, for any $w_0 \in \partial X$ such that $\int \log|z - w_0|\,d|\mu| > -\infty$, we have $\check{\mu}(w_0) = \lim \check{\mu}(w_n) = 0$. Thus $\check{\mu} = 0$ a.e. (λ), so

$$0 = \int \check{\mu}\,d\lambda = \int d\lambda(w) \int \log|z - w|\,d\mu$$

$$= \int d\mu(w) \int \log|z - w| d\lambda$$

$$= \int \log|\xi - w| d\mu(w) = \check{\mu}(\xi).$$

The proof is finished.

This proof follows Carleson [2]. Instead of the trivial Lemma 3.4.9, Carleson proves a more difficult lemma, and uses the argument above to obtain Theorem 3.4.14 at once. We have chosen a slower, more scenic route.

THEOREM 3.4.11. *Let* X *be a compact plane set, and suppose that for each* $x \in \partial X$, δ_x *is the only Jensen measure for* x *with respect to* $R(X)$. *Then* $H_b(X) = C_R(\partial X)$.

<u>Proof</u>. Let $X_1, X_2, \ldots$ be a sequence of smoothly bounded compact sets such that $X_{n+1} \subset \text{int } X_n$ for each n, and $\bigcap_1^\infty X_n = X$. Let $u \in C_R(\partial X)$; by Tietze's extension theorem, there exists $U \in C_R(X_1)$ with $u = U|\partial X$. By Theorem 3.4.10, for each n there exists $u_n \in H(X_n)$ such that $u_n|\partial X_n = U|\partial X_n$. Let $x \in \partial X$. We shall show that $u_n(x) \to u(x)$. Let σ_n be the representing measure for x on ∂X_n with respect to $H(X_n)$. Identifying each σ_n with an element of

$C(X_1)^*$, the weak-* compactness of the unit ball leads us to the existence of a measure σ on X_1 which is a weak-* cluster point of $\{\sigma_n\}$. If v is any continuous function with compact support disjoint from ∂X, then v vanishes on ∂X_n for n sufficiently large, so $\int v d\sigma_n = 0$ for large n, so $\int v d\sigma = 0$. Thus σ is supported on ∂X. We next observe that σ is a Jensen measure for x, with respect to R(X). If f is holomorphic in a neighborhood of X, and has no zeroes on ∂X, then f has no zeroes on ∂X_n for n sufficiently large; applying Theorem 3.4.10, we find $v_n \in H(X_n)$ such that $v_n | \partial X_n = \log|f| \,|\partial X_n$. Since $\log|f|$ is subharmonic in int X_n, we have $\log|f| \leq v_n$ in X_n, in particular,

$$\log|f(x)| \leq v_n(x) = \int v_n d\sigma_n = \int \log|f| d\sigma_n$$

for all large n, whence $\log|f(x)| \leq \int \log|f| d\sigma$. Since the set of $f \in R(X)$ with no zeroes on ∂X is dense in R(X), it follows that σ is a Jensen measure for x (see Section 2-5). By hypothesis, we have then $\sigma = \delta_x$. Since σ was an arbitrary cluster point of $\{\sigma_n\}$, we conclude that $\sigma_n \to \delta_x$ (weak-*). It follows that $u_n(x) = \int u_n d\sigma_n = \int U d\sigma_n$ converges to $\int U d\delta_x = u(x)$. Since

$\|u_n\|_{\partial X} \leq \|U\|$, the convergence is bounded. If μ is any measure on ∂X which annihilates $H_b(X)$, we have $\int u d\mu = \lim \int u_n d\mu = 0$ by bounded convergence, so $u \in H_b(X)$. The proof is finished.

There are various ways of showing that if X has connected complement, each boundary point of X is a peak point for P(X). The argument that we shall give uses a function-theoretic idea which has formed the basis of a long series of successes in the theory of rational approximation by the Soviet school.

If f is a function holomorphic in a neighborhood of ∞ in the Riemann sphere, we denote by $f'(\infty)$ the coefficient of $1/z$ in the Laurent expansion of f; thus, $f'(\infty) = \lim_{s \to \infty} s[f(s) - f(\infty)] = g'(0)$, where $g = f(1/z)$.

The next lemma can be quickly deduced (with $\kappa = 1/4$) from a celebrated theorem of Koebe and Bieberbach (see, e.g., Titchmarsh, *Theory of Functions*, p. 209). In this book, we wish to avoid appealing to such deep results of function theory, so we include a direct proof.

LEMMA 3.4.12. *There exists an absolute constant*

$\kappa > 0$ *with the following property: for any compact connected subset* J *of* $\mathbb{C}$, *with diameter* d, *there exists* f *holomorphic in* $\hat{\mathbb{C}}\backslash J$, *with* $|f| < 1$ *in* $\hat{\mathbb{C}}\backslash J$, $f(\infty) = 0$, *and* $|f'(\infty)| = \kappa d$.

Proof. The principal value of $\sqrt{z}$ maps $\Delta(1;\ 1)$ onto a neighborhood G of 1; choose $c > 0$ so that $G \supset \Delta(1;\ c)$. Take $\kappa = \frac{1}{2}c(4 - c^2)^{-1}$. Let U be the component of ∞ in $\hat{\mathbb{C}}\backslash J$. Choose $a, b \in J$ such that $|a - b| = d$. Since U is simply connected, there exists g holomorphic in U such that $g^2 = \frac{z - b}{z - a}$, $g(\infty) = 1$. We note that $g'(\infty) = \frac{1}{2}(a - b)$. Since $J \subset \bar{\Delta}(a;\ d)$, and $\left|\frac{z - b}{z - a} - 1\right| = \left|\frac{a - b}{z - a}\right| < 1$ outside $\bar{\Delta}(a;\ d)$, we see that $\frac{z - b}{z - a}$ maps U onto a set containing $\Delta(1;\ 1)$, and hence $g(U) \supset \Delta(1;\ c)$. It follows that $g(U)$ does not meet $\Delta(-1;\ c)$ (else there would exist $s, t \in U$ such that $g(s) = -g(t)$, whence $g^2(s) = g^2(t)$, so $s = t$, an impossibility). Let $h = \dfrac{c(z - 1)}{2(z + 1) + c^2}$; we observe that h maps $\{s\colon |s + 1| > c\}$ onto $\Delta(0;\ 1)$ (for h is the composition of $\frac{c}{z + 1}$ and $\frac{c - 2z}{2 - cz}$). Put $f = h \circ g$ in U, $f = 0$ in the bounded components of $\hat{\mathbb{C}}\backslash J$. Then f maps U into $\Delta(0;\ 1)$, $f(\infty) = 0$, and

$$f'(\infty) = \lim_{s\to\infty} c\,\frac{s(g(s) - 1))}{2g(s) + 2 - c^2}$$

$$= \frac{c}{4 - c^2} g'(\infty) = \kappa(b - a),$$

and the proof is finished.

THEOREM 3.4.13. *Let* X *be a compact plane set,* G *a component of* $\mathbb{C}\backslash X$. *If* $x \in X \cap \overline{G}$, *then* $x \in Ch(R(X))$.

Proof. For simplicity of notation, we assume $x = 0$. We shall use the "$\alpha - \beta$" criterion of Theorem 2.2.1, with $\alpha = \frac{\kappa}{2 + \kappa}$, and any β, $0 < \beta < \alpha$. Given any neighborhood V of 0, choose $r > 0$ so that $\Delta(0; \beta^{-1}r) \subset V$. Now $\Delta(0; r) \cap G$ has a component of diameter $\geq r$ (any component whose closure contains 0 will do) if r does not exceed the diameter of G, so there exists an arc $J \subset \Delta(0; r)\backslash X$ with diameter $> \frac{1}{2} r$. Applying Lemma 3.4.12, we find f holomorphic and bounded by 1 in $\hat{\mathbb{C}}\backslash J$, with $f(\infty) = 0$, $f'(\infty) > \frac{1}{2} \kappa r$. Put $g = \frac{f'(\infty) - zf}{f'(\infty) + r}$. Then g is holomorphic in $\hat{\mathbb{C}}\backslash J$, and $g(\infty) = 0$. If $s \in \Delta(0; r)\backslash J$, then $|g(s)| < 1$, and hence by the maximum modulus principle, $|g| < 1$ in $\hat{\mathbb{C}}\backslash J$. Applying Schwarz's lemma to $g(\frac{r}{z})$, we find $|g(s)| \leq \frac{r}{|s|}$ if $|s| > r$. Let $h = g|X$.

We have $h(0) = \frac{f'(\infty)}{f'(\infty) + r} > \frac{\kappa}{2 + \kappa} = \alpha$, and

$|h(s)| \leq \beta$ for all $s \notin V$, while $\|h\| < 1$. By Theorem 2.2.1, $0 \in \mathrm{Ch}(R(X))$, and the proof is finished.

The idea behind this proof is due to Gonchar [1]. We have followed a proof of Curtis [1]. The reader will observe that the hypothesis can be weakened considerably, without changing the conclusion or the proof. It suffices to assume that for arbitrarily small $r > 0$, $\Delta(x; r)\backslash X$ contains a connected set of diameter $\geq kr$, where k is independent of r.

THEOREM 3.4.14. *Let* X *be a compact plane set with a finite number of bounded complementary components* $G_1, \ldots, G_n$. *Let* $a_j \in G_j$ *for* $j = 1, \ldots, n$. *Then every real continuous function on* ∂X *can be uniformly approximated by functions of the form* $\mathrm{Re}\, f + \sum_1^n c_j \log|z - a_j|$, *where* f *is a rational function with poles only among the* a_j*'s, and* c_j *are real constants. In particular, if* X *has connected complement, then* $\mathrm{Re}\, P(X)$ *is dense in* $C_R(\partial X)$.

Proof. By Theorem 3.4.13, each point of ∂X admits a unique representing measure for $R(X)$, and hence by Theorem 3.4.11, $H_b(X) = C_R(X)$. The proof is finished by applying Corollary 3.4.7.

> This theorem is usually referred to as Walsh's theorem. It is also attributed to Lebesgue. See the bibliography.

Another corollary of Theorem 3.4.13 is a theorem of Lavrentiev:

THEOREM 3.4.15. *Let* X *be a compact plane set with connected complement and empty interior. Then* $P(X) = C(X)$.

Proof. By Theorem 3.4.13, each point of X is a peak point for $R(X) = P(X)$. By Bishop's theorem, Theorem 3.3.3, $P(X) = C(X)$.

This result contains a theorem of Walsh: *if* J *is an arc in* $\mathbb{C}$, *then* $P(J) = C(J)$.

It is possible to have $H(X) = C_R(X)$ without having $R(X) = C(X)$ (i.e., in view of Theorems 3.3.1 and 3.4.11, to have for each point of X only one Arens-Singer measure, but for many points of X, more than one representing measure). One example is the Swiss cheese X discovered by McKissick [1]. McKissick's example has the following amazing property: $R(X) \neq C(X)$, but for any disjoint closed subsets F and K of X, there exists $f \in R(X)$ such that $f = 0$ on F, $f = 1$ on K. It follows immediately that the only Jensen measures are the point masses, so $H(X) = C_R(X)$ by Theorem 3.4.11. Another example was found by Huber [1]. We present here what is probably the simplest example. It is a square Swiss cheese with square holes, constructed as follows:

For $s \in ¢$, we denote by $|s|_\infty$ the "sup norm" of s, i.e., $|s|_\infty = \max\{|\text{Re} s|, |\text{Im } s|\}$. For $c \in ¢$ and $r > 0$, we put $Q(c; r) = \{s: |s - c|_\infty < r\}$, and $\overline{Q}(c; r) = \{s: |s - c|_\infty \leq r\}$. We define the nested sequence of compact sets $\{X_n\}$ inductively, as follows. Let $X_0 = \overline{Q}(\frac{1}{2}; \frac{1}{2})$, the closed unit square. Having defined X_{n-1}, let S_n be the set of all Gaussian integers p such that $p2^{-n} \in \text{int } X_{n-1}$, and put

$$G_n = \cup \{Q(p2^{-n}; 2^{-3n}) : p \in S_n\}.$$

Let $X_n = X_{n-1} \backslash G_n$, and let $X = \bigcap_0^\infty X_n$. Since G_n consists of less than 2^{2n} squares, each with perimeter $8 \cdot 2^{-3n}$, the sum of the lengths of all the deleted squares is finite, and so $R(X) \neq C(X)$ as we saw in Section 3-2. The key fact about X is this:

> *Let* $x \in X$. *Then for infinitely many* n *there exists* $p \in S_n$ *such that* $|x - p2^{-n}| < 2^{1-n}$.

Assuming this for the moment, we show that each $x \in X$ admits only the point mass at x as an Arens-Singer measure. Put

$$u_n = \frac{\log 2 - \log|z - q_n|}{\log 2 - \log|x - q_n|},$$

where $q_n = p2^{-n}$, with $p \in S_n$ and $|x - q_n| < 2^{1-n}$. Then $u_n \in H(X)$, and (since diam $X < 2$ and $|z - q_n| \geq 2^{-3n}$ on X for every n) we have

$$0 < u_n < \frac{\log 2 + \log 2^{3n}}{\log 2 + \log 2^{n-1}} = \frac{3n + 1}{n} \leq 4,$$

while $u_n(x) = 1$, and $u_n(y) \to 0$ for all $y \neq x$ (since $q_n \to x$). Thus, if σ is any Arens-Singer measure for x,

$$1 = u_n(x) = \int u_n d\sigma \to \sigma(\{x\})$$

by bounded convergence, and so $\sigma = \delta_x$.

It remains to verify the italicized assertion above. We show that if $x \in X$, and n is not divisible by 3, there exists $p \in S_n$ such that $x \in \overline{Q}(p2^{-n}; 2^{-n})$. If $\overline{Q}(x; 2^{-n})$ is disjoint from $\overline{Q}(q2^{-m}; 2^{-2m})$ for all

$m < n$, $q \in S_m$, then any Gaussian integer p with $p2^{-n} \in \overline{Q}(x; 2^{-n})$ will do. Otherwise, there exists p such that

$$2^{-3m} < |p2^{-n} - q2^{-m}|_\infty \leq 2^{-3m} + 2^{-n}$$

for some $m < n$, $q \in S_m$, and $|p2^{-n} - x|_\infty \leq 2^{-n}$. I claim that $p \in S_n$. If not, there exists $k < n$ and $r \in S_k$ such that $|p2^{-n} - r2^{-k}|_\infty \leq 2^{-3k}$. Then

$$0 < |r2^{-k} - q2^{-m}|_\infty \leq 2^{-3m} + 2^{-3k} + 2^{-n}$$

with $r \in S_k$, $q \in S_m$, $k < n$, $m < n$. We finish the argument by showing this is impossible. We may assume $k \leq m$. Then $|q2^{-m} - r2^{-k}|_\infty > 2^{-3k}$ since $q \in S_m$, so $|q - r2^{m-k}|_\infty > 2^{m-3k}$. If $m \geq 3k$, it follows that $|q - r2^{m-k}|_\infty \geq 1 + 2^{m-3k}$, so $1 \leq 2^{-2m} + 2^{m-n}$, a contradiction since $m < n$. If $m < 3k$, then $|q - r2^{m-k}|_\infty \geq 1$, so $1 \leq 2^{-2m} + 2^{m-3k} + 2^{m-n}$. This is possible only if $3k - m = 1 = n - m$, ruled out by our hypothesis that n is not divisible by 3, or if $m = k = 1$, ruled out since S_1 is a singleton.

3-5 THE ALGEBRAS A(X) AND A_X

Let X be a compact plane set. We recall from Chapter 1 that A(X) is the algebra of all continuous functions on X which are holomorphic in the interior of X. The results of the last section enable us to give the following generalization of Wermer's maximality theorem:

THEOREM 3.5.1. *Let* X *be a compact plane set, with interior* G *and boundary* Y. *Suppose that* G *is dense in* X, *that* G *is connected, and that each point of* Y *admits a unique Jensen measure for* R(X). *Then* $A(X)|Y$ *is a maximal closed subalgebra of* C(Y); *in fact, if* B *is a function algebra on* Y *and* $B \supset R(X)|Y$, *then either* $B \subset A(X)|Y$ *or* $B = C(Y)$.

Proof. Suppose that there exists $w \in G$ such that $\phi(z) \neq w$ for all $\phi \in \text{Spec } B$. Then $(z - w)^{-1} \in B$ (Corollary 1.2.13). Since G is connected, and $B \supset R(X)|Y$, it follows that $B \supset R(Y)$ (Theorem 3.2.3). Since each point of Y lies in the closure of G, each point of Y is a peak point for R(Y) by Theorem 3.4.13, and hence $R(Y) = C(Y)$ by Theorem 3.3.3. Thus $B = C(Y)$.

Suppose on the other hand that for every $w \in G$ there exists $\phi_w \in \text{Spec } B$ such that $\phi_w(z) = w$. Let μ_w be an Arens-Singer measure on Y for ϕ_w. Then μ_w

is, *a fortiori*, an Arens-Singer measure for w with respect to $R(X)$, i.e., a representing measure for w with respect to $H(X)$. Let $f \in B$. By Theorem 3.4.11, there exists $\hat{f} \in H(X)$ such that $\hat{f}|Y = f$. For each $w \in G$, we have $\hat{f}(w) = \int \hat{f}d\mu_w = \int fd\mu_w = \phi_w(f)$. It follows that $(zf)\hat{}(w) = \phi_w(zf) = \phi_w(z)\phi_w(f) = w\hat{f}(w)$, for each $w \in G$, whence $z\hat{f} = (zf)\hat{}$ is harmonic in G, as well as $\hat{f}$. Then $\hat{f}$ is holomorphic in G, since $0 = (z\hat{f})_{\bar{z}z} = (z\hat{f}_{\bar{z}})_z = z\hat{f}_{\bar{z}z} + \hat{f}_{\bar{z}} = \hat{f}_{\bar{z}}$. Thus $\hat{f} \in A(X)$, so $f \in A(X)|Y$. The proof is finished.

We refer the reader to Gamelin and Rossi [1] for more general theorems of this type, and a deeper study of the space $H(X)$ and related questions.

The main result in this section will be a theorem of Arens which identifies the maximal ideal space of $A(X)$ with X. The theorem actually works for a larger class of algebras.

DEFINITION. Let X be a compact subset of the Riemann sphere $\hat{\mathbb{C}}$, G an open set in $\hat{\mathbb{C}}$, $G \subset X$. We define $A(X; G)$ to be the set of all functions continuous on X and holomorphic in G. We define $A(X)$ to be

$A(X; \text{int } X)$, and A_X to be $A(\hat{\mathbb{C}}, \hat{\mathbb{C}}\backslash X)$.

In general, A_X need not contain any non-constant functions. Our first result is due to Wermer [1].

LEMMA 3.5.2. *Let* X *be a compact plane set, and suppose that* A_X *contains a non-constant function. Then there exist* $f, g, h \in A_X$ *such that* $\{f, g, h\}$ *separates the points of* $\hat{\mathbb{C}}$.

<u>Proof</u>. Suppose there exists $f \in A_X$ which is not constant on $\mathbb{C}\backslash X$. Choose points s, t in $\mathbb{C}\backslash X$ such that $f(s) \neq f(t)$. Let

$$g = \frac{f - f(s)}{z - s}, \quad h = \frac{f - f(t)}{z - t}.$$

It is clear that $g, h \in A_X$. If p and q are distinct points of $\hat{\mathbb{C}}$, and $f(p) = f(q)$, then $g(p) = g(q)$ implies that $h(p) \neq h(q)$.

Now if every $f \in A_X$ is constant on $\mathbb{C}\backslash X$, then $m(X) = 0$, by Lemma 3.1.5. In particular, X must have empty interior, so $\mathbb{C}\backslash X$ is dense in $\hat{\mathbb{C}}$, and hence A_X reduces to the constants. The lemma is proved.

COROLLARY 3.5.3. *Unless* $A(X; G)$ *reduces to the*

constants, $A(X; G)$ *is a function algebra on* X.

Proof. Clearly, $A(X; G)$ is a uniformly closed subalgebra of $C(X)$. Using linear fractional transformations, we can assume that either $X = \hat{\mathbb{C}}$ and $\infty \in G$, or that $X \subset \mathbb{C}$. In the first case, $A(X; G) = A_Y$, where $Y = \hat{\mathbb{C}} \setminus G$ is a compact plane set, and Lemma 3.5.2 shows that A_Y separates the points of $\hat{\mathbb{C}}$. In the second case, z separates the points of X.

The algebras A_X have an interesting property, again first pointed out by Wermer.

LEMMA 3.5.4. *Suppose that* X *has empty interior. Then for all* $f \in A_X$, $f(X) = f(\hat{\mathbb{C}})$.

Proof. It suffices to show that if $f \in A_X$ has no zeroes on X, then f has no zeroes in $\hat{\mathbb{C}}$. Now if f has no zeroes on X, then f has at most a finite number of zeroes in $\hat{\mathbb{C}}$. Let $a_1, \ldots, a_n$ be the zeroes of f in $\mathbb{C}$ (a zero of order k being listed k times). Put $g = (z - a_1)^{-1} \ldots (z - a_n)^{-1} f$. Then $g \in A_X$, and if f has any zeroes in $\hat{\mathbb{C}}$, $g(\infty) = 0$. But g has no zeroes in $\mathbb{C}$, so $g = \exp h$ for some continuous function h on $\mathbb{C}$, necessarily holomorphic in $\mathbb{C} \setminus X$. Since

$g(\infty) = 0$, this is incompatible with the argument principle. The lemma is proved.

According to Theorem 3.4.15, if J is an arc in $\mathbb{C}$, then $P(J) = R(J) = C(J)$. The preceding results of Wermer show that the higher-dimensional analog of this theorem fails to hold: *there exists an arc* J *in* $\mathbb{C}^3$ *such that* $R(J) \neq C(J)$. For let X be an arc in $\mathbb{C}$ such that A_X does not reduce to the constants, for instance, an arc X with $m(X) \neq 0$. (The existence of such arcs was first shown by Osgood [1]. For further examples of arcs X such that A_X is non-trivial, see Denjoy [1].) Let f, g, h be the functions given by Lemma 3.5.2, and let $J = \{(f(s), g(s), h(s)) : s \in X\}$. According to Lemma 3.5.2, J is an arc in $\mathbb{C}^3$, homeomorphic to X. If F is a polynomial in 3 variables, then $F(f, g, h) \in A_X$; if $F(z_1, z_2, z_3)$ has no zeroes on J, then $F(f, g, h)$ has no zeroes on X, and hence by Lemma 3.5.4, none on $\hat{\mathbb{C}}$, so $F(f, g, h)^{-1} \in A_X$. Thus $R(J)$ is imbedded as a subalgebra of A_X (is it a proper subalgebra? no one knows.) If $w \in \hat{\mathbb{C}}\backslash X$, the map $F \to F(f(w), g(w), h(w))$ is a homomorphism of $R(J)$ onto $\mathbb{C}$, not evaluation at any point of J (since f, g, h separate the points of $\hat{\mathbb{C}}$ by Lemma 3.5.2), so $R(J) \neq C(J)$. (In other words, J is not rationally convex.)

> Rudin [1] has modified this construction to obtain an arc J in $\mathbb{C}^2$ such that $P(J) \neq C(J)$.

The next theorem is due to Arens [1]. The proof we give is a slight modification of Arens' proof, probably due to Vitushkin (see Gamelin and Garnett [1] and Zalcman [1] for further uses of the construction).

THEOREM 3.5.5. *Let* $f \in A(X; G)$, *let* $p \in X$, *and let* $\varepsilon > 0$. *Then there exists* g, *continuous on* $\hat{\mathbb{C}}$, *holomorphic in* G *and in a neighborhood of* p, *such that* $\|f - g\|_X < \varepsilon$.

Proof. We may assume that $p = 0$, and that $f(0) = 0$. If $X \neq \hat{\mathbb{C}}$, extend f to be continuous on $\hat{\mathbb{C}}$. Choose $\delta > 0$ so that $|f(s)| < \varepsilon/9$ whenever $|s| < 2\delta$. Choose $\phi \in C_c^\infty$ such that $\phi = 0$ in $\Delta(0; \delta)$, $\phi = 1$ outside $\Delta(0; 2\delta)$, and $\|\phi_{\bar{z}}\| < 2/\delta$. Put $g(w) = \frac{1}{\pi}\int \frac{f(w) - f}{w - z}\phi_{\bar{z}}\,dm$. By Corollary 3.1.3, $g(w) = f(w)\phi(w) - \frac{1}{\pi}\int \frac{f\phi_{\bar{z}}}{w - z}\,dm$. By Lemma 3.1.5, it follows that g is continuous on $\hat{\mathbb{C}}$, holomorphic in $\Delta(0;\ \delta)$. We next observe that g is holomorphic in G. Fix $w \in G$. Then

$$\frac{g(w + h) - g(w)}{h}$$

$$= \frac{1}{h\pi} \int \left[\frac{f(w + h) - f}{w + h - z} - \frac{f(w) - f}{w - z} \right] \phi_{\bar{z}}\ dm$$

$$= \frac{1}{\pi} \int \frac{f(w + h) - f(w)}{h} \frac{\phi_{\bar{z}}}{w + h - z}\ dm$$

$$- \frac{1}{\pi} \int \frac{f(w) - f}{w - z} \frac{\phi_{\bar{z}}}{w + h - z}\ dm.$$

Now $(w - z)^{-1}(f(w) - f)$ is continuous, since f is holomorphic at w; therefore, by Lemma 3.1.5, the second integral above is a continuous function of h. Evaluating the first integral by Corollary 3.1.3, we have

$$\lim_{h \to 0} \frac{g(w + h) - g(w)}{h}$$

$$= \lim_{h \to 0} \frac{f(w + h) - f(w)}{h} \phi(w + h)$$

$$+ \lim_{h \to 0} \frac{1}{\pi} \int \frac{f(w) - f(z)}{w - z} \frac{\phi_{\bar{z}}}{w + h - z}\ dm$$

$$= f'(w)\phi(w) + \frac{1}{\pi} \int \frac{f(w) - f(z)}{w - z} \frac{\phi_{\bar{z}}}{w - z}\ dm.$$

Thus $g'(w)$ exists. Finally, we estimate $\|f - g\|$. For any $w \in \mathbb{C}$,

$$|f(w) - g(w)|$$

$$= \left| f(w)(1 - \phi(w)) + \frac{1}{\pi}\int (w - z)^{-1} f \phi_{\bar{z}}\, dm \right|$$

$$\leq \|f\|_{\Delta} + \|f\|_{\Delta} \|\phi_{\bar{z}}\| \frac{1}{\pi}\int_{\Delta} |w - z|^{-1} dm$$

(where we write Δ for $\Delta(0; 2\delta)$), whence by Lemma 3.1.1 and our choice of δ it follows that $\|f - g\| < \|f\|_{\Delta}(1 + (2/\delta) \cdot 4\delta) < \varepsilon$. The theorem is proved.

COROLLARY 3.5.6. *Let* $f \in A(X; G)$, $p \in X$, $p \neq \infty$. *For each* $\varepsilon > 0$, *there exists* $g \in A(X; G)$ *such that* $\|f - f(p) - (z - p)g\| < \varepsilon$.

Proof. Immediate from Theorem 3.5.5.

THEOREM 3.5.7. *Suppose* $A(X; G)$ *contains a non-constant function. Then the maximal ideal space of* $A(X; G)$ *is* X *(with the usual identification). In particular,* Spec $A(X) = X$, *and* Spec $A_X = \hat{\mathbb{C}}$ *unless* A_X *reduces to the constants.*

Proof. By Corollary 3.5.3, $A(X; G)$ is a function algebra on X, so it suffices to show that if ϕ is a multiplicative linear functional on $A(X; G)$, there exists $p \in X$ such that $\phi(f) = f(p)$ for all f in $A(X; G)$. By using a linear fractional transformation if necessary, we may assume that either $X \subset \mathbb{C}$, or $X = \hat{\mathbb{C}}$ and $\infty \in G$. In the first case, $z \in A(X; G)$. Put $p = \phi(z)$. Clearly, $p \in X$, since $(z - p)^{-1} \in A(X; G)$ if $p \notin X$. Let $f \in A(X; G)$. By Corollary 3.5.6, there exist $g_n \in A(X; G)$ such that $(z - p)g_n \to f - f(p)$. But $\phi((z - p)g_n) = \phi(z - p)\phi(g_n) = 0$, so $\phi(f) = f(p)$. Now suppose $X = \hat{\mathbb{C}}$, and $\infty \in G$. If ϕ is not evaluation at ∞, there exists $h \in A(X; G)$ with $\phi(h) \neq h(\infty)$; replacing h by $h - h(\infty)$, we may assume $h(\infty) = 0 \neq \phi(h)$. Since $h(\infty) = 0$ and $\infty \in G$, $zh \in A(X; G)$. Put $p = \dfrac{\phi(zh)}{\phi(h)}$. Let $f \in A(X; G)$. By Corollary 3.5.6, there exist $g_n \in A(X; G)$ such that $(z - p)g_n \to f - f(p)$. Now

$$\begin{aligned}\phi((z - p)g_n) &= \frac{1}{\phi(h)} \cdot \phi(h)\phi((z - p)g_n) \\ &= \frac{1}{\phi(h)} \phi((z - p)hg_n) \\ &= \frac{1}{\phi(h)} [\phi(zh)\phi(g_n) \\ &\qquad - p\phi(h)\phi(g_n)] = 0.\end{aligned}$$

Thus $\phi(f) = f(p)$. The proof is complete.

By virtue of Theorems 3.5.5 and 3.5.7, various facts that we have learned about R(X) carry over for A(X). For instance, if $\mu \perp A(X)$, then *a fortiori* $\mu \perp R(X)$, so $\hat{\mu} = 0$ off X. It follows that $E = \{x \in X: \tilde{\mu}(x) < \infty \text{ and } \hat{\mu}(x) \neq 0\}$ has positive plane measure (unless $\mu = 0$). If $x \in E$, it follows from Theorem 3.5.5 that $\frac{1}{\hat{\mu}(x)} \frac{\mu}{z - x}$ is a complex measure which represents x. The proof of Theorem 3.3.9 carries over word for word, and hence so does its corollary: *there exists a non-zero point derivation on* A(X) *at* x *if and only if* x *is not a peak point for* A(X).

The most natural question about A(X) is, of course, when does R(X) = A(X)? The best answer to date is due to Vitushkin [1], who gives necessary and sufficient conditions in terms of "continuous analytic capacity." An exposition of Vitushkin's work is to be found in Zalcman [1]; see also Vitushkin [2]. We shall give in the next chapter a proof along function algebra lines, due to Glicksberg and Wermer, of a theorem of Mergelyan which gives a sufficient condition for R(X) = A(X). An outstanding problem is this: *if each boundary point of* X *is a peak point for* R(X), *does it follow that* R(X) = A(X)?

CHAPTER FOUR

DIRICHLET ALGEBRAS

4-7 DIRICHLET ALGEBRAS

In his 1956 paper [1], Gleason singled out one of the crucial properties of the disk algebra on the circle as offering a defining property for a class of algebras that seemed amenable to analysis. In the years that followed, his prediction was amply confirmed: Dirichlet algebras, and their generalization introduced by Hoffman, logmodular algebras, provide a setting in which an unexpectedly large amount of classical function theory on the disk finds generalization.

DEFINITION. The function algebra A on X is said to be a *Dirichlet algebra* if Re A is dense in $C_R(X)$.

We have observed that the disk algebra on the circle is a Dirichlet algebra. The big disk algebra is a Dirichlet algebra on the torus, and for the same reason: trigonometric polynomials are dense. The bicylinder algebra on the torus is very far from being Dirichlet. The Lebesgue-Walsh theorem (Theorem 3.4.14) shows that if X is a compact plane set, then $P(X)|Y$ is a Dirichlet algebra on Y, where Y is the Shilov boundary for P(X) (the boundary of $\hat{X}$, or the boundary of the unbounded component of $\mathbb{C}\setminus X$). It has been shown (Browder and Wermer [1], [2]) that there exist Dirichlet algebras on the unit interval, and proper subalgebras of the disk algebra which are Dirichlet algebras on the circle. One of the outstanding open problems in the subject is: *does there exist a non-trivial Dirichlet algebra* A *on* X, *with* Spec A = X?

The giant step in the discovery that Dirichlet algebras were a natural setting for function theory was taken by Helson and Lowdenslager [1], who worked in the setting of the big disk. Bochner's note [1] called attention to the generality of their arguments, and Wermer's theorem (Theorem

4.4.1 below) established the power of their method in the context of function algebras. The next major breakthrough was the work of Hoffman [1], who extended the results to logmodular algebras.

DEFINITION. The function algebra A on X is said to be *logmodular* if $\log|A^{-1}| = \{\log|f| : f \in A^{-1}\}$ is dense in $C_R(X)$.

Evidently, a Dirichlet algebra is necessarily logmodular ($\mathrm{Re}\, f = \log|e^f|$). In terms of annihilating measures, a function algebra A on X is Dirichlet if and only if 0 is the only real measure in $A^\perp$. This immediately implies that each $\phi \in \mathrm{Spec}\, A$ (indeed, each $\phi \in A^*$ with $\|\phi\| = \phi(1) = 1$) admits a unique representing measure. The corresponding fact for logmodular algebras is due to Hoffman.

LEMMA 4.1.1. *Let* A *be a logmodular algebra on* X, $\phi \in \mathrm{Spec}\, A$. *Then* ϕ *admits a unique representing measure.*

Proof. Suppose λ and μ are representing measures for ϕ. Then for every $f \in A^{-1}$,

$$1 = \phi(1) = \phi(f)\phi(f^{-1})$$
$$= \int f d\lambda \int f^{-1} d\mu \leq \int |f| d\lambda \int |f^{-1}| d\mu,$$

whence $1 \leq \int e^{u} d\lambda \int e^{-u} d\mu$ for all $u \in \log|A^{-1}|$, and thus for all $u \in C_R(X)$. Fix $u \in C_R(X)$. Put $F(t) = \int e^{tu} d\lambda \int e^{-tu} d\mu$, for t real. It is easy to see (expand in power series) that $\int e^{tu} d\lambda$ is a differentiable function of t, with derivative $\int ue^{tu} d\lambda$, and a similar statement holds for $\int e^{-tu} d\mu$. Hence F is a differentiable function, and for all t, $F(t) \geq 1 = F(0)$. Thus

$$0 = F'(0) = \int u d\lambda - \int u d\mu,$$

and since this holds for all $u \in C_R(X)$, we have $\lambda = \mu$, and the lemma is proved.

It was shown by Lumer [1] that all the function theory which was generalized to the context of Dirichlet algebras and then logmodular algebras depended essentially only on the conclusion of Lemma 4.1.1: the uniqueness of representing measures. This phenomenon is explained by Theorem 4.1.2 below.

We have made some reference already in Chapter

2 to the Hardy spaces associated with a function algebra. In this chapter, they become of fundamental importance. We recall that if A is a function algebra on X, and σ a probability measure on X, $H^p(\sigma)$ is defined to be the closure in $L^p(\sigma)$ of A, for $0 < p < \infty$. We define $H^\infty(\sigma)$ to be the weak-* closure of A in $L^\infty(\sigma)$ (= $L^1(\sigma)^*$). It is obvious that $H^\infty(\sigma)$ is a uniformly closed subalgebra of the Banach algebra $L^\infty(\sigma)$, which, as we saw in Chapter 1, is isometrically isomorphic to C(Y), where Y = Spec L^∞ is a totally disconnected compact Hausdorff space. It follows that $H^\infty(\sigma)$ may be regarded as a function algebra on some Y' (Y' = Y if $H^\infty(\sigma)$ separates the points of Y, otherwise Y' is obtained from Y by identifying certain points). In this chapter, we will always take σ to be a representing measure for some $\phi \in$ Spec A. In this case, one sees without difficulty that σ is multiplicative on $H^\infty(\sigma)$: $\int fg\,d\sigma = \int f\,d\sigma \int g\,d\sigma$ for all f, g $\in$ $H^\infty(\sigma)$. (Thus ϕ extends to a multiplicative linear functional $\tilde{\phi}$ on $H^\infty(\sigma)$; but note that σ is not a representing measure for $\tilde{\phi}$: it is not a measure on the space on which $H^\infty(\sigma)$ is a function algebra.) More generally, if $f \in H^p(\sigma)$ and $g \in H^q(\sigma)$, where

p and q are conjugate exponents ($\frac{1}{p} + \frac{1}{q} = 1$), then $\int fg d\sigma = \int f d\sigma \int g d\sigma$; this follows easily from Hölder's inequality.

There is a quasi-converse to Lemma 4.1.1, due to Hoffman and Rossi [1], [2].

THEOREM 4.1.2. *Let* A *be a function algebra on* X, $\phi \in$ Spec A, *and suppose that* ϕ *admits a unique representing measure* σ. *Then* $H^\infty(\sigma)$ *is a logmodular algebra on* Spec $L^\infty(\sigma)$; *in fact, more is true: for every* $u \in L^\infty_R$, *there exists* $f \in (H^\infty(\sigma))^{-1}$ *such that* $u = \log|f|$.

<u>Proof</u>. Without loss of generality, we assume that $\int u d\sigma = 0$. There exists a sequence $\{u_n\}$, $u_n \in C_R(X)$, such that $u_n \to u$ a.e. (σ), and $\|u_n\| \leq \|u\|$. By Corollary 2.2.4, there exist $g_n \in A$ such that $\operatorname{Re} g_n \leq u_n$, and $\int (u_n - \operatorname{Re} g_n) d\sigma \to 0$; without loss of generality, we may assume $\int \operatorname{Im} g_n d\sigma = 0$. Put $f_n = e^{g_n}$; then $f_n \in A$, and $|f_n| = \exp \operatorname{Re} g_n \leq e^{u_n} \leq e^{\|u\|}$. Let f be any weak-* cluster point of $\{f_n\}$ in $L^\infty(\sigma)$. Since $f_n \in A$, $f \in H^\infty$. Since $\int f_n d\sigma = \int \exp g_n d\sigma = \exp \int g_n d\sigma = \exp \int \operatorname{Re} g_n d\sigma \to 1$, we have $\int f d\sigma = 1$. Since $|f_n| \leq e^{u_n}$, we have $|f| \leq e^u$

a.e. (σ). (For if E is any Borel subset of X, $\int_E |f|d\sigma = \int fkd\sigma$, where $k = \chi_E \operatorname{sgn} \bar{f}$. But $\int fkd\sigma$ is a cluster point of $\{\int f_n k d\sigma\}$, so

$$\begin{aligned}\int_E |f|d\sigma = \int fkd\sigma &\leq \limsup \left|\int f_n k d\sigma\right| \\ &\leq \limsup \int_E |f_n| d\sigma \\ &\leq \limsup \int_E e^{u_n} d\sigma \\ &\leq \int_E e^u d\sigma \quad \text{by Fatou's lemma.}\end{aligned}$$

Thus $|f| \leq e^u$ a.e. (σ).)

We have found $f \in H^\infty(\sigma)$, $\int fd\sigma = 1$, and $\log|f| \leq u$. Similarly, we find $g \in H^\infty$, $\int gd\sigma = 1$, and $\log|g| \leq -u$. Then

$$|fg| = \exp(\log|f| + \log|g|) \leq 1,$$

and $\int fgd\sigma = \int fd\sigma \int gd\sigma = 1$, whence $fg = 1$ a.e. (σ), so $f^{-1} = g \in H^\infty$, and $\log|f| = u$. The theorem is proved.

In connection with Theorem 4.1.2, the following theorem of Gorin [1] is interesting.

THEOREM 4.1.3. *Let* X *be a metrizeable compact space, and* A *a function algebra on* X. *Suppose that for every* $u \in C_R(X)$ *there exists* $f \in A^{-1}$ *such that* $u = \log|f|$. *Then* $A = C(X)$.

<u>Proof</u>. Let $u \in C_R(X)$. Then for each real t, there exists $f_t \in A^{-1}$ such that $tu = \log|f_t|$. Now since X is metrizeable, A satisfies the second axiom of countability, and hence A^{-1} has at most countably many connected components. Since the reals are uncountable, it follows that there exist s, t, $s \neq t$, such that f_s and f_t lie in the same component of A^{-1}. Then $f_s f_t^{-1}$ lies in the component of 1 in A^{-1}; by Theorem 1.4.3, there exists $g \in A$ such that $f_s f_t^{-1} = \exp g$. Thus $(s - t)u = \log|f_s f_t^{-1}| = \mathrm{Re}\, g$, and so $u \in \mathrm{Re}\, A$. Thus $\mathrm{Re}\, A = C_R(X)$. It follows from the theorem of Hoffman and Wermer (2.7.6) that $A = C(X)$.

It would be interesting to know if there exist function algebras A (other than C(X)) on a metrizeable X with the property that for every positive continuous function u on X there exists $f \in A$ with $u = |f|$.

Gorin's theorem and 4.1.2 assure us that if σ is a unique representing measure, then the compact space on which $L^\infty(\sigma)$ is realized as an algebra of continuous functions is not metrizeable—a conclusion which should astonish nobody.

REMARK: *If* A *is a Dirichlet algebra on* X, *and* X *is totally disconnected, then* A = C(X). For if K is an open and closed subset of X, there exists $f \in A$ with $\| \text{Re } f - \chi_K \| < \frac{1}{2}$. Then f(K) and f(X\K) lie in disjoint half-planes, hence in disjoint closed disks, so $\chi_{f(K)} \in P(f(X))$, and hence $\chi_K \in A$. Thus A contains the characteristic function of every open and closed subset of X, and since linear combinations of these are dense in C(X), the conclusion follows.

Since Spec $L^\infty(\sigma)$ is totally disconnected (1.3.4), Theorem 4.1.2 provides us with examples of logmodular algebras which are not Dirichlet. For another example (the "big annulus" algebra), see Hoffman [1].

4-2 ANNIHILATING MEASURES

Throughout this section, A will be a function algebra on X, ϕ a multiplicative linear functional on A which admits a unique representing measure σ.

We denote by M the maximal ideal associated with ϕ: $M = \{f \in A: \phi(f) = 0\}$. We shall abbreviate $H^p(\sigma)$ by H^p. For $1 \leq p \leq \infty$, we put $H_0^p = \{f \in H^p : \int f d\sigma = 0\}$. It is easy to see that for $1 \leq p < \infty$, H_0^p is the closure of M in L^p, and H_0^∞ is the weak-* closure of M in L^∞.

Our objective in this section is to describe the annihilating measures for A in terms of the Lebesgue decomposition and the Radon-Nikodym theorem.

LEMMA 4.2.1. *Let* E *be an* F_σ *subset of* X *such that* $\sigma(E) = 0$. *Then there exist* $f_n \in A$, *with* $\|f_n\| \leq 1$, *such that* $f_n \to 0$ *pointwise on* E, *and* $f_n \to 1$ a.e. (σ).

Proof. We may write $E = \bigcup_1^\infty K_n$, where each K_n is closed and $K_n \subset K_{n+1}$ for all n. There exists, by the regularity of σ, an open neighborhood G_n of E such that $\sigma(G_n) < \frac{1}{n^2}$. By Urysohn's lemma, there exists $u_n \in C_R(X)$ with $u_n = 0$ on $X \backslash G_n$, $u_n = -n$ on K_n, and $-n \leq u_n \leq 0$ on X. By Corollary 2.2.4, there exist $g_n \in A$ such that $\operatorname{Re} g_n \leq u_n$ and $\operatorname{Re} \int g_n d\sigma > \int u_n d\sigma - \frac{1}{n}$. We may assume (adding an imaginary constant if necessary) that $\operatorname{Im} \int g_n d\sigma = 0$. Since $\int u_n d\sigma = \int_{G_n} u_n d\sigma \geq - n\sigma(G_n) > -\frac{1}{n}$, we have $\int g_n d\sigma > -2/n$. Let $f_n = e^{g_n}$. Then $f_n \in A$, and $|f_n| = \exp \operatorname{Re} g_n \leq \exp u_n$, so $\|f_n\| \leq 1$ and $\|f_n\|_{K_n} \leq e^{-n}$. Since $\int f_n d\sigma = \phi(e^{g_n}) = \exp \phi(g_n) = \exp \int g_n d\sigma > \exp(-2/n)$ and $\|f_n\| \leq 1$, the sequence $\{f_n\}$ converges to 1 in $L^1(\sigma)$, and hence a subsequence converges to 1 a.e. (σ). If $x \in E$, then $x \in K_n$ for all sufficiently large n, so $|f_n(x)| = \exp \operatorname{Re} g_n(x) \leq e^{-n}$ for all sufficiently large n, and the proof is finished.

If μ is any measure on X, by Lebesgue's decomposition theorem we may write $\mu = \mu_a + \mu_s$, where μ_a is absolutely continuous, and μ_s is singular with respect to σ.

The next theorem is referred to as the F. and M. Riesz theorem.

THEOREM 4.2.2. *Let* $\mu \in A^\perp$. *Then* $\mu_a \in A^\perp$ (*and hence* $\mu_s \in A^\perp$).

Proof. Since μ_s is singular with respect to σ, there exists a Borel set E such that $\sigma(E) = 0 =$

$|\mu_s|(X\backslash E)$. By regularity, we may assume that E is an F_σ. Applying Lemma 4.2.1, we find $f_n \in A$, with $\|f_n\| \leq 1$, such that $f_n \to 1$ a.e. (σ) and $f_n \to 0$ on E. Then $f_n \to 1$ a.e. (μ_a) and $f_n \to 0$ a.e. (μ_s), so for any $g \in A$, we have $0 = \int gf_n d\mu = \int gf_n d\mu_a + \int gf_n d\mu_s \to \int g d\mu_a$ by bounded convergence. Thus $\int g d\mu_a = 0$ for all $g \in A$, which was to be proved.

COROLLARY 4.2.3. *Let* $\mu \in M^\perp$. *Then* $\mu_s \in A^\perp$.

Proof. Let $c = \int d\mu$. Then $\mu - c\sigma \in A^\perp$, so $(\mu - c\sigma)_s = \mu_s \in A^\perp$ by Theorem 4.2.2.

From the general F. and M. Riesz theorem, we may quickly deduce the classical one:

COROLLARY 4.2.4. *Let* σ *be normalized Lebesgue measure on the circle* Γ, *and let* μ *be a measure on* Γ *such that* $\int z^n d\mu = 0$ *for every positive integer* n. *Then* μ *is absolutely continuous with respect to* σ.

Proof. Let A be the disk algebra on Γ; then A is a Dirichlet algebra, and the considerations of this section apply, with ϕ = evaluation at the origin. The hypothesis is that $\mu \in M^\perp$. By Corollary 4.2.3, this implies that $\mu_s \in A^\perp$. Since $M = zA$, it follows that $\bar{z}\mu_s \in M^\perp$, and again applying Corollary 4.2.3, that $\bar{z}\mu_s \in A^\perp$. By the obvious induction, we find that $\bar{z}^n\mu_s \in A^\perp$ for every non-negative integer n. Thus μ_s annihilates A and $\bar{A}$, and since $A + \bar{A}$ is dense in $C(\Gamma)$, it follows that $\mu_s = 0$. The proof is finished.

There are a number of different proofs of the F. and M. Riesz theorem in an abstract setting, going back to the ground-breaking paper of Helson and Lowdenslager [1]. We have given the proof of Forelli [1]. This argument was improved by Ahern [1] to establish the following result:

Let A *be a function algebra on* X, $\phi \in$ Spec A, σ *a representing measure for* ϕ. *Then* $\mu \in A^\perp$ *implies* $\mu_a \in A^\perp$ *if and only if every representing measure for* ϕ *is absolutely continuous with respect to* σ.

This situation was studied in detail, notably in connection with problems of rational approximation, by Glicksberg [4]. Glicksberg [3] has also found other versions of the F. and M. Riesz theorem.

Our next order of business is to describe the absolutely continuous annihilating measures. By the Radon-Nikodym theorem, if μ is a measure absolutely continuous with respect to σ, then $\mu = f\sigma$ for some $f \in L^1(\sigma)$. Let $\tilde{H} = \{f \in L^1(\sigma) : f\sigma \in A^\perp\}$. It is clear that $H_0^1 \subset \tilde{H}$; we shall prove that in fact $H_0^1 = \tilde{H}$. We begin with a theorem due to Hoffman and Wermer (unpublished; but see Wermer [5]).

THEOREM 4.2.5. *Let* $f \in H^1$, *and suppose that* $|f| \leq 1$ *a.e.* (σ). *Then there exist* $f_n \in A$, *with* $\|f_n\| \leq 1$, *such that* $f_n \to f$ *a.e.* (σ).

Proof. Since $f \in H^1$, there exist $g_n \in A$ such that $\int |f - g_n| d\sigma \to 0$. Passing to a subsequence, we may assume that $g_n \to f$ a.e. (σ). Let $u_n = \log^+|g_n|$; then $u_n \in C_R(X)$. Let $E_n = \{x \in X\colon |g_n(x)| \geq 1\}$. Then

$$\int_X u_n d\sigma = \int_{E_n} \log^+|g_n| d\sigma$$

$$\leq \int_{E_n} |g_n - f| d\sigma \leq \int_X |g_n - f| d\sigma$$

since $\log^+|g_n| \leq |g_n| - 1 \leq |g_n| - |f| \leq |g_n - f|$ on E_n. Thus $\int u_n d\sigma \to 0$. By Corollary 2.2.4, we may find $h_n \in A$ such that $\operatorname{Re} h_n \leq - u_n$, $\operatorname{Re} \int h_n d\sigma > - 2 \int u_n d\sigma$, and $\operatorname{Im} \int h_n d\sigma = 0$. Since $u_n \geq 0$, we have $|e^{h_n}| = \exp \operatorname{Re} h_n \leq e^{-u_n} \leq 1$. Also,

$$\int e^{h_n} d\sigma = \phi(e^{h_n}) = \exp \phi(h_n)$$

$$= \exp \int h_n d\sigma$$

$$= \exp \text{Re} \int h_n d\sigma > \exp(-2 \int u_n d\sigma),$$

so $\int e^{h_n} d\sigma \to 1$. Hence, $e^{h_n} \to 1$ in $L^1(\sigma)$, so passing to a subsequence, we may assume $e^{h_n} \to 1$ a.e. (σ). Let $f_n = g_n e^{h_n}$. Then $f_n \to f$ a.e. (σ), and $|f_n| = |g_n| \exp \text{Re}\, h_n \leq |g_n| \exp(-\log^+ |g_n|) \leq 1$. The theorem is proved.

COROLLARY 4.2.6. *For any* $p \geq 1$, $H^\infty = H^p \cap L^\infty$.

Proof. We observe that $H^p \subset H^1$ for $p \geq 1$ (an immediate consequence of Hölder's inequality), and $H^\infty \subset H^p$, since the weak-* topology of L^∞ is stronger than the weak L^p topology. Thus $H^\infty \subset H^p \cap L^\infty \subset H^1 \cap L^\infty$; but it is clear from Theorem 4.2.5 that $H^1 \cap L^\infty \subset H^\infty$, so all is proved.

We shall need two lemmas from the general theory of measure and integration. The first is due to Hoffman [1].

LEMMA 4.2.7. *Let* λ *be a probability measure, and* $w \in L^1(\lambda)$, $w \geq 0$. *Then*

$$\exp \int \log w d\lambda$$

$$= \inf \left\{ \int e^u w d\lambda : u \in L_R^\infty(\lambda), \int u d\lambda = 0 \right\}.$$

Proof. If $u \in L_R^\infty(\lambda)$ and $\int u d\lambda = 0$, then applying the inequality of the geometric and arithmetic means, we find

$$\exp \int \log w d\lambda = \exp \int (\log w + u) d\lambda \leq \int e^u w d\lambda,$$

which establishes the inequality in one direction. If w were bounded above, and bounded away from 0, choosing $u = \int \log w d\lambda - \log w$ would yield the opposite inequality. In general, we proceed as follows. Let $v_n^+ = \min\{n, \log^+ w\}$ and $v_n^- = \min\{n, \log^- w\}$ for each positive integer n. Put $v_n = v_n^+ - v_n^-$, and $c_n = \int v_n d\lambda$. Then $v_n \in L_R^\infty$, and $c_n \to \int \log w d\lambda$ by the monotone convergence theorem (note that this is true even if $\int \log w d\lambda = -\infty$). Put $u_n = c_n - v_n$. Then $u_n \in L_R^\infty$ and $\int u_n d\lambda = 0$. Now $-v_n \leq v_n^- \leq \log^- w$, so $e^{-v_n} w \leq \max\{1, w\}$. Since $e^{-v_n} \to \frac{1}{w}$ pointwise, we have by dominated convergence that $\int e^{-v_n} w d\lambda \to 1$. Hence

$$\lim \int e^{u_n} w d\lambda = \lim e^{c_n} \int e^{-v_n} w d\lambda$$

$$= \lim e^{c_n} = \exp \int \log w d\lambda.$$

Thus

$$\inf \left\{ \int e^u w\,d\lambda : u \in L^\infty_R, \int u\,d\lambda = 0 \right\} \leq$$

$$\leq \exp \int \log w\,d\lambda,$$

and the proof is finished.

The next lemma is due to Arens.

LEMMA 4.2.8. *Let* λ *be a finite positive measure, let* $g \in L^1_R(\lambda)$. *Suppose there exists* $\delta > 0$ *such that* $\int \log|1 - tg|\,d\lambda \geq 0$ *for all* $t \in (-\delta, \delta)$. *Then* $g = 0$ a.e. (λ).

Proof. We may assume $\delta = 1$, since it suffices to show $\delta g = 0$. For $s \in \mathbb{C}$, $|s| < 1$, define $F(s) = \int \log|1 + i(1 - s)g|\,d\lambda$. Then F is harmonic in the open unit disk. If $s = \sigma + it$, with σ and t real, we have $\log|1 + i(1 - s)g| \geq \log|1 + tg|$, so $F(s) \geq 0$ for all s, $|s| < 1$. Hence, by Harnack's inequality, we have $F(s) \geq \frac{1 - |s|}{1 + |s|} F(0)$ for all s, $|s| < 1$, and in particular,

$$F(0) \leq \frac{2}{t} F(1 - t)$$

for $0 < t < 1$. But $F(1 - t) = \int \log|1 + itg|\,d\lambda = \frac{1}{2} \int \log(1 + t^2 g^2)\,d\lambda$. By elementary calculus, one easily verifies that $t^{-1}\log(1 + t^2 x^2) \to 0$ as $t \to 0$, and $t^{-1}\log(1 + t^2x^2) \leq |x|$ when $t > 0$, for any real number x. Thus

$$F(0) \leq \frac{1}{t} \int \log(1 + t^2g^2)d\lambda \to 0$$

by dominated convergence. Hence

$$F(0) = \frac{1}{2} \int \log(1 + g^2)d\lambda = 0,$$

so $g = 0$ a.e. (λ), which was to be proved.

If we assume $g \in L_R^2$, Lemma 4.2.8 can be proved in a much more direct and elementary fashion (see Hoffman [1]), and this result would suffice, as we shall see, for most of what follows.

LEMMA 4.2.9. *For each* $g \in \tilde{H}$, $\int \log|1 - g|d\sigma \geq 0$.

Proof. According to Lemma 4.2.7,

$$\exp \int \log|1 - g|d\sigma$$

$$= \inf\left\{ \int e^u|1 - g|d\sigma : u \in L_R^\infty, \int ud\sigma = 0\right\}.$$

But as we saw in Theorem 4.1.2, if $u \in L_R^\infty$ and $\int ud\sigma = 0$, there exists $f \in (H^\infty)^{-1}$ such that $u = \log|f|$ and $|\int fd\sigma| = 1$. Thus

$$\exp \int \log|1 - g|d\sigma$$

$$= \inf\left\{ \int |f|\ |1 - g| d\sigma : (f \in (H^\infty)^{-1}, \int f d\sigma = 1 \right\}.$$

But for $f \in H^\infty$, $\int f d\sigma = 1$, we have

$$\int |f|\ |1 - g| d\sigma \geq \left| \int (f - fg) d\sigma \right| = \left| \int f d\sigma \right| = 1$$

since $g \in \tilde{H}$, and the lemma follows.

THEOREM 4.2.10. *For each* p, $1 \leq p < \infty$, $A + \bar{A}$ *is dense in* L^p; $A + \bar{A}$ *is weak-* dense in* L^∞.

Proof. Suppose that $g \in \tilde{H}$ and g is real-valued. Then $\int \log|1 - tg| d\sigma \geq 0$ for all real t by Lemma 4.2.9, and hence $g = 0$ a.e. (σ) by Lemma 4.2.8. If $g \in L^1$ and $\int fg d\sigma = \int \bar{f} g d\sigma = 0$ for all $f \in A$, then Re g and Im g belong to $\tilde{H}$, and thus $g = 0$ a.e. (σ). Thus $A + \bar{A}$ is weak-* dense in L^∞. Since $L^q \subset L^1$, where $q = \frac{p}{p - 1}$ is the conjugate exponent to p, the same argument shows that $A + \bar{A}$ is dense in L^p.

COROLLARY 4.2.11. $L^2 = H_0^2 \oplus \bar{H}^2$ *(orthogonal direct sum); thus* $\tilde{H} \cap L^2 = H_0^2$.

Proof. By Theorem 4.2.10, $H_0^2 + \overline{H}^2$ is dense in L^2; since H_0^2 and $\overline{H}^2$ are orthogonal closed subspaces, the direct sum is closed, and the corollary is proved.

THEOREM 4.2.12. $\tilde{H} = H_0^1$.

Proof. We have already observed that $H_0^1 \subset \tilde{H}$. Suppose $g \in L^\infty$ and $\int fg\,d\sigma = 0$ for all $f \in H_0^1$. Then $g - \int g\,d\sigma \in \tilde{H} \cap L^\infty \subset \tilde{H} \cap L^2$, so $g - \int g\,d\sigma \in H_0^2$ by Corollary 4.2.11, and thus $g \in H^2 \cap L^\infty$. Hence $g \in H^\infty$ by Theorem 4.2.5 and hence $\int fg\,d\sigma = 0$ whenever $f \in \tilde{H}$. Thus H_0^1 is dense in $\tilde{H}$, and of course H_0^1 is closed, so the proof is finished.

Combining Theorems 4.2.2 and 4.2.12, we have a description of annihilating measures in terms of the representing measure σ: if $\mu \in A^\perp$, then $\mu = f\sigma + \nu$, where $f \in H_0^1$ and ν is singular with respect to σ. The next theorem, due to Glicksberg and Wermer [1], extends this result to a more global description of annihilating measures for Dirichlet or logmodular algebras.

THEOREM 4.2.13. *Suppose that* A *is a function alge-*

bra on X with the property that every multiplicative linear functional on A admits a unique representing measure. Let $\mu \in A^{\perp}$. Then there exists a sequence $\{\sigma_n\}$ of representing measures, a sequence $\{f_n\}$ with $f_n \in H_0^1(\sigma_n)$, and an annihilating measure ν which is singular with respect to every representing measure for A, such that $\mu = \nu + \Sigma f_n\sigma_n$, the series converging in norm.

Proof. For each $\phi \in$ Spec A, let σ_ϕ be the representing measure for ϕ. As we observed in Section 2-6, if $\|\phi - \psi\| = 2$ then σ_ϕ and σ_ψ are singular, while if $\|\phi - \psi\| < 2$, σ_ϕ and σ_ψ are boundedly equivalent (mutually absolutely continuous) by Theorem 2.6.4 and uniqueness. Let I be the set of all the Gleason parts of Spec A. For each $\alpha \in I$, choose $\phi_\alpha \in \alpha$; let $\sigma_\alpha = \sigma_{\phi_\alpha}$. Then $\{\sigma_\alpha : \alpha \in I\}$ is a pairwise singular collection of representing measures, and for each $\phi \in$ Spec A, σ_ϕ is equivalent to σ_α for some $\alpha \in I$. For each $\alpha \in I$, let $\mu = \mu_\alpha + \nu_\alpha$, where μ_α is absolutely continuous with respect to σ_α and ν_α is singular. For each finite subset F of I, let $\nu_F = \mu - \sum_{\alpha \in F} \mu_\alpha$. Then ν_F is singular with respect to σ_β for each $\beta \in F$, since

$\nu_F = \nu_\beta - \sum_{\alpha \neq \beta} \mu_\alpha$, and ν_β and each μ_α $(\alpha \neq \beta)$ is singular with respect to σ_β. Hence ν_F is singular with respect to each μ_β, $\beta \in F$, and hence singular with respect to $\sum_F \mu_\alpha$. Thus $\| \sum_F \mu_\alpha \| = \|\mu\| - \|\nu_F\| \leq \|\mu\|$. But $\| \sum_F \mu_\alpha \| = \sum_F \|\mu_\alpha\|$, since $\{\mu_\alpha : \alpha \in F\}$ is a pairwise singular collection. Thus $\sum_F \|\mu_\alpha\| \leq \|\mu\|$ for every finite subset F of I. It follows that $J = \{\alpha \in I : \mu_\alpha \neq 0\}$ is countable, and that $\sum \mu_\alpha$ converges in norm. We put $\nu = \mu - \sum \mu_\alpha$ (what else?) and observe that ν is singular with respect to σ_β for every $\beta \in I$, and hence with respect to σ_ϕ for any $\phi \in \text{Spec } A$. For $\nu = \nu_\beta - \sum_{\alpha \neq \beta} \mu_\alpha$, and since ν_β and each μ_α with $\alpha \neq \beta$ is singular with respect to σ_β, and the series converges in norm, it follows that ν is singular with respect to σ_β. Now for each $\alpha \in I$, $\mu_\alpha \in A^\perp$ by the F. and M. Riesz theorem (Theorem 4.2.2), and hence by Theorem 4.2.12, $\mu_\alpha = f_\alpha \sigma_\alpha$ for some $f_\alpha \in H_0^1(\sigma_\alpha)$. The proof is finished by taking an enumeration of J.

4-3 APPLICATIONS

In this section, we apply the results of previous sections to obtain some theorems of classical analysis, construct some interesting function algebras, and generalize some classical function-theoretic results to an abstract setting.

We begin by using the analysis of annihilating measures obtained in the last section to obtain a theorem in polynomial approximation. The theorem is due to Mergelyan, the proof we give to Glicksberg and Wermer [1].

THEOREM 4.3.1. *Let* X *be a compact plane set with connected complement. Then* $P(X) = A(X)$.

Proof. Let Y be the boundary of X. Then P(X) is a Dirichlet algebra on Y, by Theorem 3.4.14. (We may, and shall, regard P(X) and A(X) as function algebras on Y.) Suppose μ is a measure on Y which annihilates P(X). By Theorem 4.2.13, we can write

$$\mu = \nu + \Sigma f_n \sigma_n,$$

where each σ_n is a representing measure on Y for P(X), and $f_n \in H_0^1(\sigma_n)$ (the Hardy class formed from the algebra P(X)), and where ν is singular with respect to every representing measure for P(X).

We show first that $\nu = 0$. By Theorem 3.3.1,

for each $x \in X$ such that $\tilde{\nu}(x) < \infty$ and $\hat{\nu}(x) \neq 0$, there exists a complex representing measure λ for x, with λ absolutely continuous with respect to ν. By Theorem 2.1.1, there exists a (positive) representing measure σ for x with σ absolutely continuous with respect to λ, hence with respect to ν. Since ν is singular with respect to every representing measure σ, it follows that $\hat{\nu}(x) = 0$ whenever $\hat{\nu}(x) < \infty$, and hence by Corollary 3.1.7, that $\nu = 0$.

(An alternate argument runs as follows. For each $x \in X$ such that $\int \frac{d|\nu|}{|z - x|} < \infty$, the measure $\frac{\nu}{z - x}$, singular with respect to the representing measure σ_x for x, annihilates the maximal ideal at x. By Corollary 4.2.3, $\int \frac{d\nu}{z - x} = 0$. Thus $\hat{\nu}$ vanishes a.e. on X, as well as everywhere off X, so $\nu = 0$ by Corollary 3.1.7.)

We next show that each $f_n \sigma_n$ annihilates $A(X)$. We observed in Chapter 1 that Spec $P(X) = X$ when X has connected complement. Thus each σ_n represents a point $x_n \in X$, for $P(X)$. If τ_n is a measure on Y which represents x_n for $A(X)$, τ_n *a fortiori* represents x_n for $P(X)$, so $\tau_n = \sigma_n$ by uniqueness. Since

f_n is the limit in L^1 of a sequence of functions in P(X) each vanishing at x_n, it follows that $\int gf_n d\sigma_n = 0$ for all $g \in A(X)$.

Thus each measure on Y which annihilates P(X) also annihilates A(X), so P(X) = A(X).

> Mergelyan's original proof of this theorem (see Mergelyan [1], or for a more readable exposition, the book of Rudin [2]) has the advantage of being constructive in character, and also of yielding, simultaneously, Theorem 4.3.2 below. A proof of Theorem 4.3.1 on functional analysis lines was first given by Bishop [8]. The Glicksberg-Wermer proof which we gave is also to be found in Carleson [2], stripped of all references to the general theory of Dirichlet algebras.

THEOREM 4.3.2. *Let* X *be a compact plane set, and suppose that the diameters of the components of* $\mathbb{C}\setminus X$ *are bounded away from* 0. *Then* R(X) = A(X).

<u>Proof</u>. If $2\delta > 0$ is a lower bound for the diameters of the complementary components, then for each $x \in X$, $X \cap \overline{\Delta(x;\ \delta)}$ is a compact set with connected complement. Let $f \in A(X)$. By Theorem 4.3.1, the restriction of f to $X \cap \overline{\Delta(x;\ \delta)}$ is in $P(X \cap \overline{\Delta(x;\ \delta)})$.

The theorem now follows from Bishop's localization theorem (Theorem 3.2.13).

This derivation of Theorem 4.3.2 from Theorem 4.3.1 was found by Kodama [1], and rediscovered by Garnett [2].

As an application of the (classical) F. and M. Riesz theorem, we give a construction of a Dirichlet subalgebra of the disk algebra, and some other Dirichlet algebras.

Let A be the disk algebra on the circle Γ, let σ be normalized Lebesgue measure on Γ. Let β be a strictly monotonic continuous map of $[0, 2\pi]$ onto an interval $[a, a + 2\pi]$ such that $\beta'(t) = 0$ almost everywhere (see, e.g., Riesz and Nagy [1], p. 48). Put $\alpha(e^{it}) = e^{i\beta(t)}$. Then α is a homeomorphism of Γ, which transforms σ into a measure singular with respect to σ; i.e., the measure σ_α, defined by $\sigma_\alpha(E) = \sigma(\alpha^{-1}(E))$ for Borel subsets E of Γ, or equivalently, by $\int f d\sigma_\alpha = \int f\circ\alpha d\sigma$ for $f \in C(\Gamma)$, is singular with respect to σ. Let $A_\alpha = \{f \in C(\Gamma)\colon f\circ\alpha \in A\}$. Then A_α is a Dirichlet algebra on Γ, and $A_\alpha^\perp = \{\mu_\alpha\colon \mu \in A^\perp\}$. By the F. and M. Riesz theorem (Corollary 4.2.4), each $\mu \in A^\perp$ is absolutely continuous with respect to σ, and hence μ_α is absolutely continuous with respect to σ_α. Thus, if $\mu \in A^\perp$ and $\nu \in A_\alpha^\perp$, μ and ν are singular, so $\|\mu + \nu\| = \|\mu\| + \|\nu\|$. By Lemma 2.4.8, it follows that $A^\perp + A_\alpha^\perp$ is weak-* closed. Since $A^\perp + A_\alpha^\perp$ is weak-* dense in $(A \cap A_\alpha)^\perp$, it follows that $(A \cap A_\alpha)^\perp = A^\perp + A_\alpha^\perp$. If $\mu + \nu$ is real, with $\mu \in A^\perp$ and $\nu \in A_\alpha^\perp$, then the absolutely continuous and singular parts of $\mu + \nu$ are real, i.e., μ and ν are real, so $\mu = \nu = 0$. Thus $A \cap A_\alpha$ is a Dirichlet algebra on the circle, properly contained in A.

Now suppose that $\alpha \circ \alpha$ is the identity map of Γ. Let $B = \{f \in A: f \circ \alpha = f\}$. Let X be the space obtained from Γ by identifying the orbits of α to points. One may verify that there are only two possibilities: either α has no fixed points, when α is orientation-preserving, and X is homeomorphic to Γ; or α has two fixed points, when α reverses orientation, in which case X is homeomorphic to $[0, 1]$. Since $C(X)$ may be identified with $\{f \in C(\Gamma): f = f \circ \alpha\}$, B may be regarded as a closed subalgebra of $C(X)$. We show that B is a Dirichlet algebra on X by showing that if λ is a real measure on Γ, annihilating B, then $\lambda \perp \{f \in C(\Gamma): f = f \circ \alpha\}$, i.e., that $\lambda(E) = -\lambda(\alpha(E))$ for every Borel subset E of Γ. Let Ω be the set of all such "odd" measures λ. Clearly, Ω is weak-* closed, and $B^{\perp}$ is the weak-* closure of $A^{\perp} + \Omega$. Now if $\mu \in A^{\perp}$ and $\nu \in \Omega$, then

$$\|\mu\| = \frac{1}{2}\|\mu + \mu_{\alpha}\| = \frac{1}{2}\|\mu + \nu + \mu_{\alpha} - \nu\|$$

$$= \frac{1}{2}\|\mu + \nu + \mu_{\alpha} + \nu_{\alpha}\| \leq \frac{1}{2}(\|\mu + \nu\| + \|\mu_{\alpha} + \nu_{\alpha}\|)$$

$$= \|\mu + \nu\|,$$

where we used the fact that μ and μ_{α} are singular, and $\nu_{\alpha} = -\nu$ since $\nu \in \Omega$. Applying Lemma 2.4.8 again, we find that $A^{\perp} + \Omega$ is weak-* closed, and hence $B^{\perp} = A^{\perp} + \Omega$. Suppose $\lambda \in B^{\perp}$ is real. Then $\lambda = \mu + \nu$, where $\mu \in A^{\perp}$, $\nu \in \Omega$. Hence

$$\lambda + \lambda_{\alpha} = \mu + \mu_{\alpha} + \nu + \nu_{\alpha} = \mu + \mu_{\alpha} \text{ is real,}$$

and hence $\mu = 0$. Thus $\lambda = \nu \in \Omega$, and B is a Dirichlet algebra on X. We next show that B is a maximal subalgebra of C(X). Let B_1 be a closed subalgebra of $C(\Gamma)$, with $B_1 \supset B$ and with $f = f \circ \alpha$ for every $f \in B_1$. Then every $\lambda \in B_1^{\perp}$ is of the form $\mu + \nu$, with $\mu \in A^{\perp}$, $\nu \in \Omega$, and $B_1 \neq C(X)$ if and only if there exists $\mu + \nu \in B_1^{\perp}$ with $\mu \neq 0$. Now for any $f \in B_1$, $f\mu + f\nu \in B_1^{\perp}$, so $f\mu + f\nu = \mu_1 + \nu_1$, with $\mu_1 \in A^{\perp}$, $\nu_1 \in \Omega$. But $f\nu \in \Omega$ since $f = f \circ \alpha$, so

$f\mu - \mu_1 \in \Omega$. Since $f\mu - \mu_1$ is absolutely continuous, it follows that $f\mu - \mu_1 = 0$. Thus $f\mu \in A^\perp$ for all $f \in B_1$. Thus μ annihilates the algebra generated by A and B_1; since $\mu \neq 0$, this algebra is proper, and we conclude from Wermer's maximality theorem that $B_1 \subset A$, and hence $B_1 \subset B$, concluding the argument.

it can be shown that Spec $(A \cap A_\alpha)$, and Spec B when α reverses orientation, are homeomorphic to the 2-sphere. When α preserves orientation, Spec B is homeomorphic to the real projective plane. See Browder and Wermer [2] for the details. Since $A^\perp + A_\alpha^\perp$ is closed, it follows from Lemma 2.7.7 that $A + A_\alpha$ is closed, and hence $A + A_\alpha = C(\Gamma)$. (If α is any orientation-reversing homeomorphism of Γ, it is shown in the above paper that $A + \bar{A}$ is dense in $C(\Gamma)$, though $A + \bar{A}$ need not be closed, nor an algebra, when α is not singular.)

Let J be an arc in the complex plane. Let ψ be the Riemann map of the unit disk Δ onto $\hat{\mathbb{C}}\backslash J$. It is known that Ψ extends continuously to $\bar{\Delta}$. For each $s \in \Gamma$, there exists a unique $\alpha(s) \in \Gamma$ such that $\psi(s) = \psi(\alpha(s))$, and one may verify that α is a homeomorphism of Γ, and $\alpha \circ \alpha$ is the identity. The map $f \to f \cdot \psi$ is an isomorphism of A_J onto B. Thus A_J is a Dirichlet algebra on J if the boundary identification α induced by ψ is singular. Arcs J with this property were constructed in Browder and Wermer [1].

For the remainder of this section, we return to the setting of Section 2: A is a function algebra on X, $\phi \in \operatorname{Spec} A$ admits a unique representing measure σ, M is the maximal ideal associated with ϕ.

We shall next obtain, in this context, a theorem due to Szegö when A is the disk algebra. It is of fundamental importance in the prediction theory of stationary stochastic processes (see, e.g., the book of Grenander and Szegö [1]).

THEOREM 4.3.3. *Let* μ *be a positive measure on* X; *by the Lebesgue decomposition and Radon-Nikodym theorem,* $\mu = w\sigma + \nu$, *where* $w \in L^1(\sigma)$ *and* ν *is singular with respect to* σ. *Let* $0 < p < \infty$. *Then*

$$\inf \left\{ \int |1 - f|^p d\mu : f \in M \right\} = \exp \int \log w d\sigma.$$

<u>Proof</u>. Let $f \in M$. Then

$$\int \log|1 - f| d\sigma \geq \log|\phi(1 - f)| = 0$$

since σ is a Jensen measure for ϕ. Since

$$\int |1 - f|^p w d\sigma \geq \exp \int (\log w + p \log|1 - f|) d\sigma$$

(inequality of the geometric and arithmetic means) it follows that

$$\exp \int \log w d\sigma \leq \inf\left\{ \int |1 - f|^p w d\sigma : f \in M \right\}.$$

On the other hand, by Lemma 4.2.7, $\exp \int \log w d\sigma =$

$$\inf \left\{ \int e^u w d\sigma : u \in L^\infty_R(\sigma), \int u d\sigma = 0 \right\},$$

while by Theorem 4.1.2, for each $u \in L^\infty_R(\sigma)$ with $\int u d\sigma = 0$, there exists $f \in (H^\infty)^{-1}$ such that $\log|f| = \frac{u}{p}$ and $\int f d\sigma = 1$. Thus

$$\begin{aligned} \exp \int \log w d\sigma & \\ &= \inf \left\{ \int |f|^p w d\sigma : f \in (H^\infty)^{-1}, \int f d\sigma = 1 \right\} \\ &\geq \inf \left\{ \int |f|^p w d\sigma : f \in H^\infty, \int f d\sigma = 1 \right\} \\ &= \inf \left\{ \int |1 - f|^p w d\sigma : f \in H^\infty_0 \right\}. \end{aligned}$$

From Theorem 4.2.5, we see that each $f \in H^\infty_0$ is the pointwise a.e. (σ) limit of a bounded sequence in M; it follows from bounded convergence that

$$\exp \int \log w d\sigma \geq \inf \left\{ \int |1 - f|^p w d\sigma : f \in M \right\}.$$

Thus

$$\exp \int \log w d\sigma = \inf \left\{ \int |1 - f|^p w d\sigma : f \in M \right\},$$

and it remains to show only that

$$\inf \left\{ \int |1 - f|^p d\mu : f \in M \right\}$$

$$= \inf \left\{ \int |1 - f|^p w d\sigma : f \in M \right\}.$$

Let $f \in M$. By Lemma 4.2.1 (the heart of the F. and M. Riesz theorem), there exist $g_n \in A$ such that $g_n \to 1$ a.e. (σ), $g_n \to 0$ a.e. (ν), with $\int g_n d\sigma = 1$ and $\| g_n \| < 2$ for all n. Then $\phi((1 - f)g_n) = \phi(1 - f)\phi(g_n) = 1$, so $(1 - f)g_n = 1 - h_n$ for some $h_n \in M$. Applying bounded convergence, we have

$$\int |1 - h_n|^p d\mu = \int |(1 - f)g_n|^p (w d\sigma + d\nu)$$

$$\to \int |1 - f|^p w d\sigma.$$

Thus

$$\inf \left\{ \int |1 - h|^p d\mu : h \in M \right\} \leq \int |1 - f|^p w d\sigma,$$

so

$$\inf \left\{ \int |1 - f|^p d\mu : f \in M \right\}$$

$$\leq \inf \left\{ \int |1 - f|^p w d\sigma : f \in M \right\}.$$

Since the opposite inequality is obvious, the proof is concluded.

Szegö proved this theorem (for A the disk algebra) with the stronger hypothesis that μ is absolutely continuous; the general case is due to Kolmogorov and Krein. The most interesting case is, naturally, $p = 2$; the theorem for any p can in fact be deduced from the theorem for $p = 2$, though there seems no good reason to do so.

An interesting corollary of Szegö's theorem is the following, taken from Hoffman's book [2].

THEOREM 4.3.4. *Let* σ *be normalized Lebesgue measure on the circle* Γ, *let* $1 \leq p < \infty$, *let* $g \in L^p(\sigma)$. *Then the linear span of* $\{z^n g$: *n a non-negative integer*$\}$ *is dense in* $L^p(\sigma)$ *if and only if* i) $g \neq 0$ *a.e.* (σ), *and* ii) $\int \log|g|d\sigma = -\infty$.

Proof. Let S be the closed linear span of $\{z^n g: n \geq 0\}$. Suppose ii) holds. Then, taking A to be the disk algebra and applying Theorem 4.3.3, we have

$$\inf\left\{\int |1 - f|^p\ |g|^p d\sigma: f \in M\right\} = 0,$$

or, since $M = zA$,

$$\inf\left\{\int |g - zfg|^p d\sigma: f \in A\right\} = 0.$$

Since $fg \in S$ whenever $f \in A$, and since $|z| = 1$, we have $\bar{z}g \in S$. By an obvious inductive argument, we conclude that $\bar{z}^n g \in S$ for every n. Now if $h \in L^q(\sigma)$, where $q = \frac{p}{p-1}$, and $\int fh d\sigma = 0$ for every $f \in S$, it follows that $\int z^n gh d\sigma = 0$ for every integer n, positive or negative, so $gh = 0$ a.e. (σ). If i) holds, it follows that $h = 0$ a.e. (σ), and hence $S = L^p(\sigma)$.

On the other hand, if $S = L^p(\sigma)$, then i) obviously holds, and since $\bar{z}g \in S$, we have

$$\begin{aligned} 0 &= \inf \left\{ \int |\bar{z}g - fg|^p d\sigma : f \in A \right\} \\ &= \inf \left\{ \int |1 - zf|^p \, |g|^p d\sigma : f \in A \right\} \\ &= \inf \left\{ \int |1 - f|^p \, |g|^p d\sigma : f \in M \right\}, \end{aligned}$$

so $\int \log|g| d\sigma = -\infty$ by Theorem 4.3.3. The proof is finished.

Theorem 4.3.4 leads naturally to the question: which closed subspaces S of $L^2(\sigma)$ (or of $H^2(\sigma)$) are invariant under multiplication by z? There are some obvious candidates: if $E \in L^\infty(\sigma)$ (or $H^\infty(\sigma)$) and $|E| = 1$ a.e., then $S = EH^2(\sigma) = \{Ef: f \in H^2(\sigma)\}$ is evidently such a space. In 1949, Beurling [1] proved that every invariant subspace of $H^2(\sigma)$ is of this form. Beurling's proof used deep results from function theory, but he observed that the function E was essentially the orthogonal projection of 1 on S. It was the inspired contribution of Helson and Lowdenslager [1] to make this observation the basis of the proof; they thus not only obtained Beurling's theorem in a more general setting, but a much simpler proof for the classical case. There is now a large literature on various generalizations of Beurling's theorem; see the books of Hoffman [2] and Helson [1] for a start, and for further references. We shall next give the natural generalization of Beurling's theorem in the context of this chapter.

THEOREM 4.3.5. *Let* S *be a closed subspace of* $L^2(\sigma)$, *with the properties that*

i) *if* $f \in A$ *and* $g \in S$, *then* $fg \in S$;

ii) *the closed linear span of*

$\{fg\colon f \in M,\ g \in S\}$ *is not dense in* S.

Then there exists $E \in L^\infty(\sigma)$, *with* $|E| = 1$ *a.e.* (σ), *such that* $S = EH^2(\sigma) = \{Ef\colon f \in H^2(\sigma)\}$; E *is uniquely determined (up to multiplication by a constant of modulus* 1).

Proof. Let T be the closed linear span of $\{fg: f \in M, g \in S\}$. Since T is a proper closed subspace of S, there exists $E \in S$, $\int |E|^2 d\sigma = 1$, such that E is orthogonal to T, i.e., $\int fg\overline{E}d\sigma = 0$ for all $f \in M$, $g \in S$. Taking $g = E$, we have in particular that $\int f|E|^2 d\sigma = 0$ for all $f \in M$. Thus $|E|^2\sigma$ is a probability measure annihilating M, hence a representing measure for ϕ. By uniqueness, we conclude that $|E|^2\sigma = \sigma$, i.e., that $|E| = 1$ a.e. (σ). It follows that multiplication by E is an isometry of $L^2(\sigma)$ into itself, so $EH^2(\sigma)$ is a closed subspace of S. Suppose that $g \in S$ is orthogonal to $EH^2(\sigma)$, Then

$$\int \overline{fE}g d\sigma = 0$$

for all $f \in A$; but for $f \in M$, $fg \in T$, so

$$\int fg\overline{E}\, d\sigma = 0;$$

thus $\overline{E}g$ is orthogonal to $A + \overline{M}$. By Corollary 4.2.11, we conclude that $\overline{E}g = 0$, and since $|E| = 1$ a.e. (σ), that $g = 0$. Thus $EH^2(\sigma) = S$. If also $S = FH^2(\sigma)$ where $|F| = 1$ a.e. (σ), then $E = Ff$ for some $f \in H^2(\sigma)$, so $E\overline{F} = f \in H^2(\sigma)$, and similarly, $\overline{E}F \in H^2(\sigma)$. Hence $E\overline{F}$ is orthogonal to $H_0^2(\sigma) + \overline{H}_0^2(\sigma)$, and hence $E\overline{F}$ = const. a.e. by Corollary 4.2.11. The proof is concluded.

COROLLARY 4.3.6. *Let* S *be a closed subspace of* $H^2(\sigma)$, *such that*

i) *if* $f \in A$ *and* $g \in S$, *then* $fg \in S$;

ii) 1 *is not orthogonal to* S.

Then there exists $E \in H^\infty(\sigma)$, $|E| = 1$ a.e. (σ), *such that* $S = EH^2(\sigma)$.

<u>Proof</u>. Since 1 is orthogonal to $\{fg: f \in M, g \in S\}$, ii) implies that the second hypothesis of Theorem 4.3.5 is satisfied. The function E produced by Theorem 4.3.5 belongs to $H^2(\sigma) \cap L^\infty(\sigma)$, so $E \in H^\infty(\sigma)$ by Corollary 4.2.6.

We note that when A is the disk algebra on the circle, hypothesis ii) of Corollary 4.3.6 is unnecessary; replace S by $\bar{z}^n S$ if necessary.

4-4 ANALYTIC STRUCTURE IN THE MAXIMAL IDEAL SPACE

Again in this section we keep fixed a function

algebra A on X with a multiplicative linear functional ϕ which admits a unique representing measure σ. We denote by M the maximal ideal associated with ϕ, and we denote by P the Gleason part of ϕ: thus $P = \{\psi \in \text{Spec } A: \|\phi - \psi\| < 2\}$. This section is devoted to proving the theorem (due to Wermer [3] when A is a Dirichlet algebra, extended by Hoffman [1] to the case of logmodular A, and proved by Lumer [1] in the present generality) that unless P reduces to a singleton, it is an analytic disk.

THEOREM 4.4.1. *Suppose* $P \neq \{\phi\}$. *Then there exists a map* Φ *of the open unit disk* $U = \Delta(0; 1)$ *onto* P *such that for every* $f \in A$, $\hat{f}\circ\Phi$ *is a bounded holomorphic function on* U *(where* $\hat{f}$ *is the Gelfand transform of* f*). The map* Φ *is a homeomorphism if* P *is given the metric topology, and thus a one-one continuous map when* P *is given the weak (Gelfand) topology.*

<u>Proof</u>. We shall use several lemmas.

LEMMA 4.4.2. *Let* $\psi \in P$. *Then* ψ *admits a unique representing measure* μ, *and* μ *is boundedly equivalent to* σ *(i.e., there exist constants* a, b *with*

$0 < a \leq b < \infty$ *such that* $a\mu \leq \sigma \leq b\mu$).

Proof. By Theorem 2.6.4 (or 2.6.5) there exist representing measures λ for ϕ and μ for ψ, and constants a, b with $0 < a \leq b < \infty$ such that $a\mu \leq \lambda \leq b\mu$. Since σ is the only representing measure for ϕ, we have $\lambda = \sigma$. Suppose ν is any representing measure for ψ. Then $a(\nu - \mu)$ annihilates A, and since $\sigma - a\mu \geq 0$, it follows that $\sigma + a(\nu - \mu)$ is a representing measure for ϕ. From the uniqueness of σ, it follows that $\nu = \mu$. The lemma is proved.

In view of Lemma 4.4.2, if $\psi \in P$ and μ is a representing measure for ψ, the spaces $H^2(\sigma)$ and $H^2(\mu)$ are identical as sets of (equivalence classes of) functions; as Hilbert spaces, they have distinct but equivalent norms. Thus H_0^2 is the closure of M in H^2, where $H^2 = H^2(\sigma) = H^2(\mu)$, and closure may be taken in either the $L^2(\sigma)$ or $L^2(\mu)$ sense without altering the meaning.

Our next lemma tells us that, loosely speaking, M is a principal ideal; more precisely, it does contain the assertion that the associated maximal ideal in H^∞ is principal.

LEMMA 4.4.3. *There exists* $Z \in H_0^2$ *such that* $|Z| = 1$ *a.e., and such that* $H_0^2 = ZH^2$.

Proof. The function Z may be constructed either as in the proof of Theorem 2.6.4 or as in Beurling's theorem of the last section. Let us repeat the latter argument. Choose $\psi \in P$, $\psi \neq \phi$, and let μ be the representing measure for ψ. Let E be the projection of 1 on H_0^2 in $H^2(\mu)$. Thus $E \in H_0^2$, and $1 - E$ is orthogonal to H_0^2 in $L^2(\mu)$. Let $c^2 = \int |E|^2 d\mu$. Then $c^2 > 0$, for otherwise $\int f d\mu = 0$ for all $f \in M$, contradicting the assumption that $\psi \neq \phi$. We put $Z = c^{-1}E$. If $f \in A$, then $fE \in H_0^2$, so $\int fE(1 - \bar{E})d\mu = 0$, or $\int fE d\mu = \int f|E|^2 d\mu$; in particular, $\int E d\mu = c^2$. Since μ is multiplicative on H^2, it follows that

$$c^2\psi(f) = \int fE d\mu = \int f|E|^2 d\mu$$

for all $f \in A$, i.e., $c^{-2}|E|^2\mu = |Z|^2\mu$ is a representing measure for ψ. Hence, by Lemma 4.4.2, $|Z| = 1$ a.e. From $|Z| = 1$ a.e. it is obvious that ZH^2 is a closed subspace of H^2, and from the multiplicativity of σ that $ZH^2 \subset H_0^2$. To show that $ZH^2 = H_0^2$, it suffices then to show that no non-zero element of H_0^2 is orthogonal to ZH^2. Suppose $g \in H_0^2$ and $\int \bar{g}Zfd\mu = 0$ for all $f \in A$. If $f \in A$, then $gf \in H_0^2$, so $\int gf(1 - \bar{E})d\mu = 0$, or $\int g\bar{Z}fd\mu = c^{-1} \int gfd\mu$. Hence, for all $f \in A$ with $\int fd\mu = 0$, we have $\int g\bar{Z}fd\mu = 0$. Thus $g\bar{Z}$ is orthogonal to $\bar{A}$ as well as A. But $A + \bar{A}$ is dense in $L^2(\mu)$ by Theorem 4.2.10 (and Lemma 4.4.2). Hence $g\bar{Z} = 0$ a.e., and hence $g = 0$ a.e. The proof is concluded.

The next lemma is a simple corollary.

LEMMA 4.4.4. *For each* $s \in U$, *the orthogonal complement of* $(Z - s)H^2$ *in* $H^2(\sigma)$ *consists of the constant multiples of* $(1 - \bar{s}Z)^{-1}$.

__Proof__. For any $f \in H^2$,

$$\int f(Z - s)(1 - s\bar{Z})^{-1}d\sigma = \int fZd\sigma = 0,$$

since $|Z| = 1$ a.e. and $fZ \in H_0^2$. Thus $(1 - \bar{s}Z)^{-1}$ is orthogonal to $(Z - s)H^2$.

Suppose $g \in H^2$ and g is orthogonal to $(Z - s)H^2$. Then

$$0 = \int \bar{g}(Z - s)fd\sigma = \int \bar{g}(1 - s\bar{Z})Zfd\sigma$$

for all $f \in H^2$. Thus $g(1 - \bar{s}Z)$ is orthogonal to

H_0^2 in view of Lemma 4.4.3, and hence $g(1 - \bar{s}Z) =$ const. The lemma is proved.

We now proceed to the proof of Theorem 4.4.1. For each $s \in U$, we define the linear functional Φ_s on A by

$$\Phi_s(f) = \int f(1 - s\bar{Z})^{-1} d\sigma$$

for each $f \in A$; since $(1 - s\bar{Z})^{-1}$ is bounded, the definition makes sense and $\Phi_s \in A^*$. Since $(1 - s\bar{Z})^{-1} = \sum_0^\infty s^n \bar{Z}^n$, the series converging uniformly, we have $\Phi_s(1) = 1$. Since $\Phi_s(f)$ is the inner product of f with $(1 - \bar{s}Z)^{-1}$, Lemma 4.4.4 tells us that $\Phi_s(f) = 0$ if and only if $f \in (Z - s)H^2$. Hence the kernel of Φ_s is an ideal, and thus $\Phi_s \in$ Spec A for each $s \in U$.

For $f \in A$ and $s \in U$, let $\tilde{f}(s) = \Phi_s(f)$. Then $\tilde{f}(s) = \sum_0^\infty [\int f\bar{Z}^n d\sigma] s^n$, so $\tilde{f}$ is holomorphic in U. Since $\|\Phi_s\| = 1$ (Lemma 1.2.9), we have $|\tilde{f}(s)| \leq \|f\|$ for all $s \in U$, $f \in A$. By Schwarz's lemma it follows that

$$|\tilde{f}(s) - \tilde{f}(t)| \leq 2|s - t|\ |1 - \bar{s}t|^{-1}$$

whenever $s, t \in U$, $f \in A$, $\|f\| < 1$. Thus

$$\|\Phi_s - \Phi_t\| \leq 2|s - t|\ |1 - \bar{s}t|^{-1}$$

for all s, t ϵ U. In particular,

$$\|\Phi_s - \phi\| = \|\Phi_s - \Phi_0\| \leq 2|s| < 2.$$

so $\Phi_s \epsilon P$ for all $s \epsilon U$.

Now by Theorem 4.2.5, there exist $f_n \epsilon A$, $\|f_n\| \leq 1$, such that $f_n \to Z$ a.e. (σ). Then $\Phi_s(f_n) = \int f_n(1 - s\bar{Z})^{-1}d\sigma \to \int Z(1 - s\bar{Z})^{-1}d\sigma$. But $\int Z(1 - s\bar{Z})^{-1}d\sigma = \sum_0^\infty \int s^n Z^{1-n}d\sigma = s$. Thus $\Phi_s(f_n) - \Phi_t(f_n) \to s - t$, so

$$\|\Phi_s - \Phi_t\| \geq |s - t|.$$

From the inequalities $|s - t| \leq \|\Phi_s - \Phi_t\| \leq \dfrac{2|s - t|}{|1 - \bar{s}t|}$ it is clear that Φ is a homeomorphism of U into P, when P is given the metric topology. We have already observed that $\tilde{f} = \hat{f}\cdot\Phi$ is holomorphic for every f ϵ A. It remains to show that Φ is onto. Let $\theta \epsilon P$, let ν be the representing measure for θ. Let $s = \int Z d\nu$; s is well-defined by Lemma 4.4.2, $|s| \leq 1$ since $|Z| = 1$ a.e., and $|s| = 1$ is ruled out since Z is not constant a.e. (σ) (for $\int Z d\sigma = 0$) and hence not constant a.e. (ν). Thus s ϵ U. If f ϵ A, by Lemma 4.4.4 we can write

$$f = \frac{c}{1 - \bar{s}Z} + (Z - s)g$$

for some $g \in H^2$. Using the multiplicativity of ν on H^2, we find

$$\theta(f) = \int f d\nu = c \int \frac{d\nu}{1 - \bar{s}Z} + \int (Z - s) g d\nu$$

$$= c \sum_0^\infty \bar{s}^n \int Z^n d\nu + \int (Z - s) d\nu \int g d\nu$$

$$= c \sum |s|^{2n} = c(1 - |s|^2)^{-1}.$$

On the other hand,

$$\Phi_s(f) = \int \frac{f}{1 - s\bar{Z}} d\sigma = \int \frac{fZ}{Z - s} d\sigma$$

$$= c \int \frac{d\sigma}{|1 - \bar{s}Z|^2} + \int fZ d\sigma$$

$$= c \sum_{m,n} \bar{s}^n s^m \int Z^n \bar{Z}^m d\sigma$$

$$= c \sum |s|^{2n} = c(1 - |s|^2)^{-1}.$$

Thus $\Phi_s = \theta$. We have shown that Φ maps U onto P, and the proof of Theorem 4.4.1 is finished.

Special cases of Theorem 4.4.1 are worth examining. If Y is a compact plane set with connected complement, then Y can be identified as we have seen with the maximal ideal space of P(X), where X is the boundary of Y, and P(X) is a

Dirichlet algebra. In this case, the map Φ provided by Theorem 4.4.1 is the Riemann map of U onto a component of the interior of Y. It is easy to see that the map $f \to \tilde{f}$ developed in the proof of Theorem 4.4.1 extends to a map of $H^{\infty}(\sigma)$ *onto* $H^{\infty}(U)$, the algebra of all bounded holomorphic functions on U. As a consequence, one obtains the theorem of Farrell: *every bounded holomorphic function on the interior of* Y *can be approximated, uniformly on compact sets, by a uniformly bounded* (*on* Y) *sequence of polynomials*. See Wermer [5] for more details.

Another example to look at is the big disk algebra described in Chapter I. In that chapter, we described a one-one continuous mapping of the half-plane into the maximal ideal space which we now see is (modulo the equivalence of disk and half-plane) the mapping Φ promised by Theorem 4.4.1. This example show that Φ need not be a homeomorphism when P is taken with the Gelfand topology; for as we saw in Chapter I, the functions in A are taken into almost-periodic functions on the half-plane, which define a topology quite distinct from the ordinary topology on the half-plane.

One more example must be mentioned. Let σ be Lebesgue measure on the circle. Then $H^{\infty}(\sigma)$ is a logmodular algebra, as we have seen, and one of the Gleason parts is rather obvious. But there exist many other parts in Spec $H^{\infty}(\sigma)$, as was first pointed out by Gleason. The full story is quite complicated, and is to be found in Hoffman [3].

We must not conclude this section without mentioning some generalizations. A function algebra A on X is called *hypo-Dirichlet* if there exist $f_1,\ldots,f_n \in A^{-1}$ such that the linear combinations $\mathrm{Re}\, g + \sum_1^n c_j \log|f_j|$ (where $g \in A$ and c_j are real constants) is dense in $C_R(X)$. For example, if X is a compact plane set with finitely many complementary components, then R(X) is a hypo-Dirichlet algebra on the boundary of X (Theorem 3.4.14). Wermer [8] showed that if A is a hypo-Dirichlet algebra, and $\phi \in$ Spec A belongs to a non-trivial Gleason part, then there exists an analytic disk through ϕ. O'Neill [1] showed that in this situation, the part of ϕ could be given the structure of analytic space; he also showed, using the argument of Bishop which we saw in Theorem 2.6.4, that

Wermer's conclusion could be obtained with the weaker hypothesis that the uniform closure of Re A has finite codimension in $C_R(X)$. Abstract function theory in the context of hypo-Dirichlet algebras was developed by Ahern and Sarason [1]. Using their work, O'Neill and Wermer [1] showed that each non-trivial part in a hypo-Dirichlet algebra could be regarded as a finite-sheeted covering of the unit disk. Finally, Gamelin [1] showed that each such part is in fact a finite open Riemann surface.

Finally, we bring up an open problem. The results of this chapter, and the theory of hypo-Dirichlet algebras, exhibit a close relation between certain phenomena in function algebras and results from the theory of functions of one complex variable. Is there a higher-dimensional analog? For instance, are there any hypotheses of a general character which would yield the existence, in the maximal ideal space of a function algebra, of complex analytic structure of dimension greater than one?

APPENDIX

COLE'S COUNTEREXAMPLE TO THE PEAK POINT CONJECTURE

THEOREM. *There exists a function algebra* $\tilde{A}$ *on a compact metrizeable space* $\tilde{X}$ *such that*

i) Spec $\tilde{A} = \tilde{X}$;

ii) $\tilde{A} \neq C(\tilde{X})$;

iii) *every point of* $\tilde{X}$ *is a peak point for* $\tilde{A}$.

<u>Proof</u>. Let X be a compact subset of ¢ with the properties: a) $R(X) \neq C(X)$, b) for each $x \in X$, δ_x is the only Jensen measure for x with respect to R(X). (For an example of such an X, see pp. 193-195.) Let $A = R(X)$. Choose a countable dense subset $\{f_m\}$ of A^{-1}; since X has no interior, $\{f_m\}$ is then dense in A.

We shall construct the space $\tilde{X}$, and the algebra $\tilde{A}$ on $\tilde{X}$, with a continuous map π of $\tilde{X}$ onto X, in such a way that the functions $f \circ \pi$ ($f \in A$) belong to $\tilde{A}$, and such that each $f_m \circ \pi$ admits an n-th root in $\tilde{A}$ for every positive integer n. (In Cole's thesis [1], a more general construction is carried out, so that every function in $\tilde{A}$ admits n-th roots; in this way, Cole obtains (besides the example given here) algebras where every Gleason part is trivial, and no non-zero point derivations exist, while the Shilov boundary is a proper subset of the maximal ideal space.)

Let I be the set of all ordered pairs (m, n) of positive integers, with $n \geq 2$. For each $(m, n) \in I$, let $Y_{mn} = \{1,\dots,n\}$, and let Y be the Cartesian product $\prod_I Y_{mn}$; for $y \in Y$, we denote by $y(m, n)$ the coordinate of y in Y_{mn}. We define $\tilde{X}$ (as a set, not as a topological space) by $\tilde{X} = X \times Y$. Let π be the natural projection of $\tilde{X}$ onto X : $\pi(x, y) = x$.

For each $(m, n) \in I$, let $f_m^{1/n}$ denote the principal determination of the n-th root of f_m; thus each $f_m^{1/n}$ is a bounded (not necessarily continuous) function on X. For each n, let ω_n be a primitive n-th root of unity. For each $(m, n) \in I$, we define the function g_{mn} on $\tilde{X}$ by

$$g_{mn}(x, y) = f_m^{1/n}(x)\omega_n^{y(m,n)},$$

and we put

$$\mathcal{G} = \{f \circ \pi : f \in A\} \cup \{g_{mn} : (m, n) \in I\}.$$

We give $\tilde{X}$ the $\mathcal{G}$ topology, i.e., the weakest topology which makes each $F \in \mathcal{G}$ continuous.

We observe that the countable subset $\{f_m \circ \pi\} \cup \{g_{mn}\}$ of $\mathcal{G}$ separates the points of $\tilde{X}$: indeed, if $\tilde{x} = (x, y)$ and $\tilde{x}' = (x', y')$ are distinct points of $\tilde{X}$, then either $x \neq x'$, in which case $f_m(x) \neq f_m(x')$ for some m, so $(f_m \circ \pi)(\tilde{x}) \neq (f_m \circ \pi)(\tilde{x}')$, or $x = x'$ and $y(m, n) \neq y'(m, n)$ for some $(m, n) \in I$, in which case $g_{mn}(\tilde{x}) = f_m^{1/n}(x)\omega_n^{y(m,n)} \neq f_m^{1/n}(x)\omega_n^{y'(m,n)} = g_{mn}(\tilde{x}')$. It follows that $\tilde{X}$ is a Hausdorff space, satisfying the second axiom of countability.

Let $\tilde{A}$ be the uniformly closed algebra generated by $\mathcal{G}$. Clearly, $\tilde{A}$ is a commutative Banach algebra with unit; we shall show that $\tilde{X}$ is compact (and hence that $\tilde{A}$ is a function algebra on $\tilde{X}$) by showing that Spec $\tilde{A} = \tilde{X}$. Since $\tilde{A}$ is a separating algebra of continuous functions on $\tilde{X}$, it suffices to show that for each $\phi \in$ Spec $\tilde{A}$ there exists $\tilde{x}_\phi \in \tilde{X}$ such that $\phi(F) = F(\tilde{x}_\phi)$ for every $F \in \tilde{A}$. Let $\phi \in$ Spec $\tilde{A}$. Then the map $f \to \phi(f \circ \pi)$ is a multiplicative linear functional on A; since Spec A = X, there exists $x_\phi \in A$ such that $\phi(f \circ \pi) = f(x_\phi)$ for every $f \in A$. For each $(m, n) \in I$, we have $g_{mn}^n = f_m \circ \pi$; hence

$$\phi(g_{mn})^n = \phi(g_{mn}^n) = \phi(f_m \circ \pi) = f_m(x_\phi),$$

so there exists $y_\phi(m, n) \in Y_{mn}$ such that $\phi(g_{mn}) = f_m^{1/n}(x_\phi)\omega_n^{y_\phi(m,n)}$. Let $y_\phi = \{y_\phi(m, n)\}$ and $\tilde{x}_\phi = (x_\phi, y_\phi)$; we have then $\phi(F) = F(\tilde{x}_\phi)$ for every $F \in \mathcal{G}$, and hence for every $F \in \tilde{A}$.

Thus $\tilde{A}$ is a function algebra on $\tilde{X}$, and Spec $\tilde{A} = \tilde{X}$. Since $\tilde{X}$ satisfies the second axiom of countability, it is metrizeable.

To show that $\tilde{A} \neq C(\tilde{X})$, it suffices (since $A \neq C(X)$) to show that if $f \in C(X)$ and $f \circ \pi \in \tilde{A}$, then $f \in A$. We shall show even more: there exists a continuous linear map P of $C(\tilde{X})$ onto $C(X)$, such that $P(f \circ \pi) = f$ for every $f \in C(X)$, and $P(\tilde{A}) \subset A$. We define P by "averaging over the fibers of π".

For each positive integer N, let $S_N = \{y \in Y : y(m, n) = 1 \text{ if } \max\{m, n\} > N\}$. Let c_N be the cardinality of S_N (c_N is clearly finite). For $F \in C(\tilde{X})$, define

$$P_N F(x) = c_N^{-1} \sum_{y \in S_N} F(x, y).$$

Thus, for each N, P_N maps $C(\tilde{X})$ into B(X), the space of bounded functions on X; clearly, P_N is linear, $\|P_N\| = 1$, and $P_N(f\circ\pi) = f$ for every $f \in C(X)$. Let $\mathcal{F} = \{f\circ\pi : f \in C(X)\} \cup \{g_{mn} : (m, n) \in I\} \cup \{\bar{g}_{mn} : (m, n) \in I\}$. Let F be a polynomial in $\mathcal{F}$. We shall show: $P_N F \in C(X)$ *and is independent of* N, *for* N *sufficiently large*; if F *is a polynomial in* $\mathcal{G}$, *then* $P_N F \in A$ *for* N *sufficiently large*. We map assume, since P_N is linear, that F is a monomial:

$$F = (f\circ\pi) g_{m_1 n_1}^{k_1} \bar{g}_{m_1 n_1}^{\ell_1} \cdot\dots\cdot g_{m_r n_r}^{k_r} \bar{g}_{m_r n_r}^{\ell_r},$$

where $f \in C(X)$, $(m_j, n_j) \in I$, and k_j, ℓ_j are non-negative integers, for $1 \leq j \leq r$. Let

$$g = \prod_{j=1}^{r} |f_{m_j}|^{(k_j+\ell_j)/n_j},$$

so $g \in C(X)$, and let $\omega_j = \omega_{n_j}^{k_j-\ell_j}$ for $1 \leq j \leq r$. Then

$$F(x, y) = f(x)g(x) \prod_{j=1}^{r} \omega_j^{y(m_j,n_j)},$$

so $P_N F = fgc_N^{-1} \sum_{S_N} \prod_{1}^{r} \omega_j^{y(m_j,n_j)}$. Thus $P_N F \in C(X)$, and if $\omega_1 = \dots = \omega_r = 1$, then clearly $P_N F = fg$ for all N. On the other hand, if say $\omega_1 \neq 1$, then $P_N F = 0$ for all large N. In fact, if $N > \max\{m_1, n_1\}$, then putting $S_{N,j} = \{y \in S_N : y_{m_1 n_1} = j\}$ for $1 \leq j \leq n_1$, we have

$$\sum_{S_N} \prod_1^r \omega_j^{y(m_j,n_j)} = \sum_{j=1}^{n_1} \sum_{y \in S_{N,j}} \prod_1^r \omega_k^{y(m_k,n_k)}$$

$$= \sum_{j=1}^{n_1} \omega_1^j \sum_{y \in S_{N,j}} \prod_2^r \omega_k^{y(m_k,n_k)} = 0,$$

since ω_1 is an n_1-th root of unity, and $\omega_1 \neq 1$. Thus $P_N F = 0$ for $N > \max\{m_1, n_1\}$. If F is a polynomial in $\mathcal{G}$, then $f \in A$, $\ell_j = 0$ for $1 \leq j \leq r$, and we may assume $0 \leq k_j < n_j$ for $1 \leq j \leq r$. Then for large N, either $P_N F = f$ or $P_N F = 0$; in either case, $P_N F \in A$. We have proved the italicized assertion.

We define PF, when F is a polynomial in $\mathcal{F}$, as $\lim_{N\to\infty} P_N F$. We have: $PF \in C(X)$, $P(f \circ \pi) = f$ whenever $f \in C(X)$, $PF \in A$ whenever F is a polynomial in $\mathcal{G}$, and $\|P\| = 1$. Since polynomials in $\mathcal{F}$ are dense in $C(\tilde{X})$ by the Stone-Weierstrass theorem, we may extend P to $C(\tilde{X})$ by continuity. Then P maps $C(\tilde{X})$ into $C(X)$, $P(\tilde{A}) \subset A$, $P(f \circ \pi) = f$ for all $f \in C(X)$, and $\|P\| = 1$. We have proved assertion ii) of the theorem.

It remains to show that each point of $\tilde{X}$ is a peak point for $\tilde{A}$. Let $\tilde{x} = (x, y) \in \tilde{X}$. Let μ be a representing measure for $\tilde{x}$. Let ν be the measure on X defined by $\nu(E) = \mu(\pi^{-1}(E))$ for Borel sets $E \subset X$; equivalently, $\int f d\nu = \int f \circ \pi \, d\mu$ for all $f \in C(X)$. Since μ is a positive measure, we see that $\text{supp } \mu \subset \pi^{-1}(\text{supp } \nu)$.

For any $(m, n) \in I$, we have

$$\int |f_m|^{1/n} d\nu = \int |f_m \circ \pi|^{1/n} d\mu = \int |g_{mn}| d\mu$$

$$\geq \left| \int g_{mn} d\mu \right| = |g_{mn}(\tilde{x})|$$

$$= |f_m(x)|^{1/n}.$$

Thus $|f_m(x)| \leq [\int |f_m|^{1/n} d\nu]^n$ for all n, m. Since $\{f_m\}$ is dense in A, it follows that $|f(x)| \leq [\int |f|^{1/n} d\nu]^n$ for every $f \in A$, every positive integer n, and hence $|f(x)| \leq \exp \int \log|f| d\nu$ for every $f \in A$ (see p. 125). Thus ν is a Jensen measure for x with respect to A, and hence, by our choice of A, $\nu = \delta_x$. It follows that $\text{supp } \mu \subset \pi^{-1}(\{x\}) = \tilde{X}_x$. Now for every $(m, n) \in I$,

$$\left| \int g_{mn} d\mu \right| = |g_{mn}(\tilde{x})|$$

$$= |f_m(x)|^{1/n}$$

$$= \int |g_{mn}| d\mu$$

since $|g_{mn}| = |f_m(x)|^{1/n}$ on $\tilde{X}_x$. Hence g_{mn} is constant on supp μ for every $(m, n) \in I$. Since $\{g_{mn} : (m, n) \in I\}$ separates the points of $\tilde{X}_x$, it follows that supp $\mu = \{\tilde{x}\}$, i.e., that $\mu = \delta_{\tilde{x}}$.

We have shown that for each $\tilde{x} \in \tilde{X}$, $\delta_{\tilde{x}}$ is the only representing measure for $\tilde{x}$, i.e., that $\tilde{x} \in Ch(\tilde{A})$. Since $\tilde{X}$ is metrizeable, it follows that each $\tilde{x} \in \tilde{X}$ is a peak point for $\tilde{A}$, and the proof is complete.

BIBLIOGRAPHY

AHERN, P. R.

[1] *On the generalized F. and M. Riesz theorem,* Pacific J. Math. 15 (1965), 373-376.

AHERN, P. R. and SARASON, D.

[1] *The* H^p *spaces of a class of function algebras,* Acta Mathematica 117 (1967), 123-163.

ARENS, R.

[1] *The maximal ideals of certain function algebras,* Pacific J. Math. 8 (1958), 641-648.

ARENS, R. and SINGER, I. M.

[1] *Function values as boundary integrals,* Proc. Amer. Math. Soc. 5 (1954), 735-745.

[2] *Generalized analytic functions,* Trans. Amer. Math. Soc. 81 (1956), 379-393.

BEURLING, A.

[1] *On two problems concerning linear transformations in Hilbert space,* Acta Math. 81 (1949), 239-255.

BISHOP, E.

[1] *Subalgebras of functions on a Riemann sur-*

face, Pacific J. Math. 8 (1958), 29-50.

[2] *A minimal boundary for function algebras*, Pacific J. Math. 9 (1959), 629-642.

[3] *A generalization of the Stone-Weierstrass theorem*, Pacific J. Math. 11 (1961), 777-783.

[4] *A general Rudin-Carleson theorem*, Proc. Amer. Math. Soc. 13 (1962), 140-143.

[5] *Holomorphic completions, analytic continuation, and the interpolation of semi-norms*, Annals of Math. 78 (1963), 468-500.

[6] *Representing measures for points in a uniform algebra*, Bulletin Amer. Math. Soc. 70 (1964), 121-122.

[7] *Abstract dual external problems*, Notices of the Amer. Math. Soc. 12 (1965), p. 123.

BISHOP, E. and DE LEEUW, K.

[1] *The representation of linear functionals by measures on sets of extreme points*, Annales Inst. Fourier (Grenoble) 9 (1959), 305-331.

BOCHNER, S.

[1] *Generalized conjugate and analytic functions without expansions*, Proc. Nat. Acad. Sciences, 45 (1959), 855-857.

BONSALL, F. F.

[1] *On the representation of points of a convex set*, J. London Math. Soc. 38 (1963), 332-334.

BROWDER, A.

[1] *On a theorem of Hoffman and Wermer*, in Function Algebras, Scott, Foresman and Company, 1966, 88-89.

[2] *Point derivations on function algebras*, J. of Functional Analysis, 1 (1967), 22-27.

BROWDER, A. and WERMER, J.

[1] *Some algebras of functions on an arc*, J. Math. Mech., 12 (1963), 119-130.

[2] *A method for constructing Dirichlet algebras*, Proceedings Amer. Math. Soc. 15 (1964), 546-552.

CARLESON, L.

[1] *Interpolations by bounded analytic functions and the Corona problem*, Annals of Math. 76 (1962), 547-559.

[2] *Mergelyan's theorem on uniform polynomial approximation*, Math. Scand. 15 (1964), 167-175.

COHEN, P. J.

[1] *Factorization in group algebras*, Duke Math. J. 26 (1959), 199-205.

[2] *A note on constructive methods in Banach algebras*, Proceedings Amer. Math. Soc. 12 (1961), 159-163.

COLE, B. J.

[1] *One-point parts and the peak point conjecture*, Ph.D. dissertation, Yale Univ., 1968.

CREESE, T. M.

[1] *Norm interpolation in function algebras and the piecemeal recovery of maximal ideal spaces*, in Function Algebras, Scott Foresman Chicago 1966, pp. 70-83.

CURTIS, P. C., JR.

[1] *Peak points for algebras of analytic functions*, to appear.

CURTIS, P. C., JR. and FIGÁ-TALAMANCA, A.

[1] *Factorization theorems for Banach algebras*,

in Function Algebras, Scott Foresman and Company, Chicago, 1966, pp. 169-185.

DE BRANGES, L.

[1] *The Stone-Weierstrass theorem*, Proc. Amer. Math. Soc. 10 (1959), 822-824.

DENJOY, A.

[1] *Sur la continuité des fonctions analytiques singulières*, Bull. Soc. Math. France 60 (1932), 27-105.

DUNFORD, N. and SCHWARTZ, J.

[1] *Linear operators* (Part I), Interscience, New York, 1958.

FORELLI, F.

[1] *Analytic measures*, Pacific J. Math. 13 (1963), 571-578.

GAMELIN, T. W.

[1] *Embedding Riemann surfaces in maximal ideal spaces*, J. Functional Analysis, 2 (1968), 123-146.

[2] *Uniform algebras*, Prentice Hall, Englewood Cliffs, 1969.

GAMELIN, T. W. and GARNETT, J.

[1] *Constructive techniques in rational approximation*, to appear.

GAMELIN, T. and ROSSI, H.

[1] *Jensen measures and algebras of analytic functions*, in Function Algebras, Scott-Foresman and Co., 1966, 15-35.

GARNETT, J.

[1] *A topological characterization of Gleason parts*, Pacific J. Math. 20 (1967), 59-63.

[2] *On a theorem of Mergelyan*, Pacific J. Math.

26 (1968), 461-467.

GELFAND, I. M.

[1] *Normierte Ringe*, Mat. Sbornik N.S. 9 (51) (1941), 3-24.

GLEASON, A. M.

[1] *Function algebras*, Seminars on Analytic Functions, Institute for Advanced Study, Princeton, 1957, vol II.

[2] *Finitely generated ideals in Banach algebras*, J. Math. Mech. 13 (1964), 125-132.

[3] *A characterization of maximal ideals*, J. Analyse Math. 19 (1967), 171-172.

GLICKSBERG, I.

[1] *Measures orthogonal to algebras and sets of antisymmetry*, Trans. Amer. Math. Soc. 105 (1962), 415-435.

[2] *Maximal algebras and a theorem of Rado*, Pacific J. Math. 14 (1964), 919-941.

[3] *The abstract F. and M. Riesz theorem*, J. of Functional Analysis 1 (1967), 109-122.

[4] *Dominant representing measures and rational approximation*, Trans. Amer. Math. Soc. 130 (1968), 425-462.

GLICKSBERG, I. and WERMER, J.

[1] *Measures orthogonal to a Dirichlet algebra*, Duke Math. J. 30 (1963), 661-666.

GONCHAR, A. A.

[1] *On the minimal boundary of* A(E), Izv. Akad. Nauk SSSR Ser. Mat. 27 (1963), 949-955. (Russian).

GORIN, E. A.

[1] *Moduli of invertible elements in a normed*

algebra, Vestnik Moskov. Univ. Ser. I, Mat. Meh. 1965, no. 5, 35-39. (Russian).

GRENANDER, U. and SZEGÖ, G.

[1] *Toeplitz forms and their applications*, Univ. of California Press, Berkeley and Los Angeles, 1968.

GUNNING, R. C. and ROSSI, H.

[1] *Analytic functions of several complex variables*, Prentice-Hall, Englewood Cliffs, N.J., 1965.

HALLSTROM, A. P.

[1] *On bounded point derivations and analytic capacity*, to appear in J. Functional Analysis.

HELSON, H.

[1] *Lectures on invariant subspaces*, Academic Press, New York, 1964.

HELSON, H. and LOWDENSLAGER, D.

[1] *Prediction theory and Fourier series in several variables*, Acta Math. 99 (1958), 165-202.

HERVÉ, M.

[1] *Sur les représentations intégrales à láide des points extrémaux dans un ensemble compact convexe metrizable*, C. R. Acad. Sci., Paris, 253 (1961), 366-368.

HOFFMAN, K.

[1] *Analytic functions and logmodular Banach algebras*, Acta Math. 108 (1962), 271-317.

[2] *Banach spaces of analytic functions*, Prentice-Hall, Englewood Cliffs, 1962.

[3] *Bounded analytic functions and Gleason parts*, Annals of Math. (2)86 (1967), 74-111.

HOFFMAN, K. and ROSSI, H.

[1] *Function theory and multiplicative linear functionals*, Trans. Amer. Math. Soc. 116 (1965), 536-543.

[2] *Extensions of positive weak*- continuous functionals*, Duke Math. J.34(1967), 453-466.

HOFFMAN, K. and SINGER, I. M.

[1] *Maximal subalgebras of* C(X), Amer. J. Math. 79 (1957), 295-305.

[2] *On some problems of Gelfand*, Uspekhi Mat. Nauk 87(1959), 99-114. (Russian).

[3] *Maximal algebras of continuous functions*, Acta Math. 103 (1960), 217-241.

HOFFMAN, K. and WERMER, J.

[1] *A characterization of* C(X), Pacific J. Math. 12 (1962), 941-944.

HORMANDER, L.

[1] *An introduction to complex analysis in several variables*, Van Nostrand, Princeton, 1966.

HUBER, A.

[1] *Über Potentiale, welche auf vorgegebenen Mengen verschwinden*, Commentarii Math. Helvetici 43 (1968), 41-50.

KALLIN, E.

[1] *A nonlocal function algebra*, Proc. Nat. Acad. Sciences 49 (1963), 821-824.

[2] *Polynomial convexity: the spheres problem*, Proceedings of the Conference on Complex Analysis, Minneapolis 1964, 301-304. Springer-Verlag, Berlin, 1965.

KODAMA, L. K.

[1] *Boundary measures of analytic differentials*

and uniform approximation on a Riemann surface, Pacific J. Math. 15(1965),1261-1277.

LEBESGUE, H.

[1] *Sur le problem de Dirichlet*, Rend. Palermo 29 (1907), 371-402.

LOOMIS, L.

[1] *An introduction to abstract harmonic analysis*, Van Nostrand, New York, 1953.

LUMER, G.

[1] *Analytic functions and the Dirichlet problem*, Bulletin Amer. Math. Soc. 70 (1964), 98-104.

PHELPS, R.

[1] *Lectures on Choquet's theorem*, Van Nostrand, Princeton, 1966.

MELNIKOV, M. S.

[1] *A bound for the Cauchy integral along an analytic curve*, Mat. Sbornik 71(113),(1966), 503-515. (Russian).

[2] *On the structure of Gleason parts of the algebra* R(E), Funkcional. Anal. i Priložen 1 (1967), 97-100. (Russian).

MERGELYAN, S. N.

[1] *Uniform approximations to functions of a complex variable*, Amer. Math. Soc. Transl. 101 (1954).

MIRKIL, H.

[1] *The work of Šilov on commutative semi-simple Banach algebras*, Notas de Matematica 20, Rio de Janeiro.

NAIMARK, M.

[1] *Normed rings*, P. Noordhoff, Groningen, 1959.

O'NEILL, B. V., JR.

[1] *Parts and one-dimensional analytic spaces*, American J. Math. 90 (1968), 84-97.

O'NEILL, B. V., JR. and WERMER, J.

[1] *Parts as finite-sheeted coverings of the disk*, American J. Math. 90 (1968), 98-107.

OSGOOD, W. F.

[1] *A Jordan curve of positive area*, Trans. Amer. Math. Soc. 4 (1903), 107-112.

REITER, H.

[1] *Contributions to harmonic analysis:* VI, Annals of Math. 77 (1963), 552-562.

RICKART, C.

[1] *General theory of Banach algebras*, Van Nostrand, Princeton, 1960.

RIESZ, F.

[1] *Sur les valeurs moyennes des fonctions*, J. London Math. Soc. 5 (1930), 120-121.

RIESZ, F. and SZ.-NAGY, B.

[1] *Functional analysis*, Frederick Ungar, New York, 1955.

RUDIN, W.

[1] *Subalgebras of spaces of continuous functions*, Proc.Amer.Math.Soc.7(1956), 825-830.

[2] *Real and complex analysis*, McGraw Hill, New York, 1966.

SIDNEY, S. J.

[1] *Point derivations in certain sup-norm algebras*, Trans.Amer.Math.Soc.131(1968), 119-127.

[2] *Properties of the sequence of closed powers of a maximal ideal in a sup-norm algebra*, Trans.Amer.Math.Soc. 131(1968), 128-148.

SIDNEY, S. J. and STOUT, E. L.

[1] *A note on interpolation*, Proc. Amer. Math. Soc. 19 (1968), 380-382.

STEEN, L. A.

[1] *On uniform approximation by rational functions*, Proc.Amer.Math.Soc.17(1966),1007-1011.

STOLZENBERG, G.

[1] *A maximal ideal space with no analytic structure*, J.of Math.and Mech.12(1963),103-111.

[2] *Polynomially and rationally convex sets*, Acta Math. 109 (1963), 259-289.

[3] *The analytic part of the Runge hull*, Math. Annalen 164 (1966), 286-290.

[4] *Uniform approximation on smooth curves*, Acta Math. 115 (1966), 185-198.

VITUSHKIN, A. G.

[1] *Necessary and sufficient conditions on a set in order that any continuous function analytic at the interior points of the set may admit of uniform approximation by rational functions*, Soviet Math.Dokl.7(1966),1622-1625.

[2] *Analytic capacity of sets in problems of approximation theory*, Russian Math. Surveys 22 (1967), 139-200.

WALSH, J. L.

[1] *The approximation of harmonic functions by harmonic polynomials and harmonic rational functions*, Bull.Amer.Math.Soc.35 (1929), 499-544.

WERMER, J.

[1] *Polynomial approximation on an arc in* C^3, Annals of Math.62 (1955), 269-270.

[2] *The hull of a curve in* C^n, Annals of Math. 68 (1958), 550-561.

[3] *Dirichlet algebras*, Duke Math. J. 27 (1960), 373-382.

[4] *The space of real parts of a function algebra*, Pacific J.Math. 13 (1963), 1423-1426.

[5] *Seminar über Funktionen-Algebren.* Lecture notes in Mathematics, 1 (1964), Springer-Verlag, Berlin Gottingen-Heidelberg.

[6] *Approximation on a disk*, Math. Annalen 155 (1964), 331-333.

[7] *Bounded point derivations on certain Banach algebras*, J.of Functional Analysis, 1 (1967), 28-36.

[8] *Analytic disks in maximal ideal spaces*, American J. Math.86 (1964), 161-170.

WILKEN, D. R.

[1] *Lebesgue measure of parts for* R(X), Proc. Amer. Math. Soc. 18 (1967), 508-512.

ZALCMAN, L.

[1] *Analytic capacity and rational approximation*, Lecture Notes in Mathematics 50 Springer-Verlag, Berlin-Heidelberg, New York, 1968.